The Sheldon Book of Verse

COMPILED BY

P. G. SMITH

AND

J. F. W

OXFORD UNIVERSITY PRESS

Oxford University Press, Walton Street, Oxford OX2 6DP

OXFORD NEW YORK TORONTO
DELHI BOMBAY CALCUTTA MADRAS KARACHI
KUALA LUMPUR SINGAPORE HONG KONG TOKYO
NAIROBI DAR ES SALAAM CAPE TOWN
MELBOURNE AUCKLAND MADRID

and associated companies in
BERLIN IBADAN

Oxford is a trade mark of Oxford University Press

Selection, arrangement, and editorial matter
© *Oxford University Press 1959*

FIRST PUBLISHED 1959

REPRINTED FROM SHEETS OF THE FIRST EDITION
1961, 1965, 1972, 1980, 1984, 1989, 1993

PRINTED IN HONG KONG

PREFACE

THE perfect anthology is one that contains *all* the poems you really like; but if you are fortunate enough to care greatly for poetry, it might require special transport. Some volumes, less ambitious, nevertheless, have established their hold on the affections: *The Oxford Book of English Verse*, even if it dies (in effect) at Swinburne; *The Golden Treasury*, battered but handy, in many a travelling bag; Walter de la Mare's *Come Hither*, which mingles quiet music with amiably irrelevant notes, without ever losing the true thread of poetry; or General Wavell's unpretentiously titled *Other Men's Flowers*. Some of these may claim to have been representative collections of English poetry; but they hold their place, in fact, by some virtue of choice or of spirit.

The aim of *The Sheldon Book of Verse* is more limited, in the sense that the four volumes are planned as a graded course for use in schools up to the fifth form. But they contain enough poems for private reading as well as for class use, and we hope that the variety of choice and arrangement may encourage the reader to browse in them, so that they may become more than mere textbooks. We have tried to give a widely representative selection of the older poets while putting a strong emphasis on modern poetry; more than two-fifths of the poems are copyright ones. Each book contains several poems of a length unusual in anthologies, and some poems which may tax the reader's understanding and appreciation, together with poems by American authors, and a selection of light verse. The emphasis varies according to the book: Books I and II contain more narrative verse and strongly marked rhythms and images, while from Books III to IV there is a transition to more philosophical verse, or love poetry.

The poems are arranged, not in rigid groups by subject-matter, but so that one leads to another along some thread of similarity or contrast, which may depend upon mood, subject, style, form, age, or authorship.

To facilitate more formal study, there are brief notes at the end and indexes which may suggest a grouping of poems by subject, period, style, and so on.

If this anthology succeeds in giving pleasure, in opening for its readers a way to the enjoyment and appreciation of poetry, it will have achieved its aim.

P. G. S.
J. F. W.

Taunton
December, 1958

CONTENTS

5

CONTENTS

ACKNOWLEDGEMENTS

The Oxford University Press for 'April' by G. F. Bradby.

Messrs. Sidgwick & Jackson Ltd. for 'A Little Dog's Day' by Rupert Brooke.

Miss D. E. Collins and Messrs. J. M. Dent and Sons Ltd. for 'The Donkey' from *The Wild Knight and Other Poems* by G. K. Chesterton.

Mrs. H. M. Davies and Messrs. Jonathan Cape Ltd. for 'Leisure' from *The Collected Poems of W. H. Davies*.

Mr. Robert Frost, Messrs. Jonathan Cape Ltd., and The Henry Holt Co. Inc. for 'Stopping by Woods on a Winter Evening' from *The Collected Poems of Robert Frost*.

The Author's Representatives and Messrs. Macmillan & Co. Ltd. for 'The Yarn of the Nancy Bell' from *Bab Ballads* by W. S. Gilbert.

The Trustees of the Hardy Estate and Messrs. Macmillan & Co. Ltd. for 'The Night of Trafalgar' from *The Dynasts* and 'Weathers' from *The Collected Poems of Thomas Hardy*.

Mr. Ralph Hodgson and Messrs. Macmillan & Co. Ltd. for 'Time, you old gipsy man' and 'The Bells of Heaven' from *Poems*.

Mr. Richard Hughes and Messrs. Chatto & Windus Ltd. for 'Old Cat Care'.

Mrs. George Bambridge and Messrs. Macmillan & Co. Ltd. for 'The Song of the Little Hunter' and 'The Law of the Jungle' from *The Second Jungle Book* and 'A Smuggler's Song' from *Puck of Pook's Hill* by Rudyard Kipling.

The Macmillan Co., New York, for 'The Flower-fed Buffaloes' and 'Daniel' by Vachel Lindsay.

The Literary Trustees of Walter de la Mare and Messrs. Faber & Faber Ltd. for 'The Scarecrow', 'Silver', and 'Lord of Tartary' by Walter de la Mare.

Dr. John Masefield, O.M., and The Society of Authors for 'Sea Fever' and 'Cargoes'.

Mrs. Alida Monro for 'Milk for the Cat' by Harold Monro.

Messrs. Methuen & Co. Ltd. for 'Smells' from *Chimney Smoke* by Christopher Morley.

Messrs. Constable & Co. Ltd. for 'The Whistle' by Charles Murray.

Mr. Ogden Nash and Messrs. J. M. Dent & Sons Ltd. for 'The Tale of Custard the Dragon'.

Capt. Francis Newbolt, C.M.G., and Messrs. John Murray Ltd. for 'Gillespie' from *Poems Old and New* by Sir Henry Newbolt.

Mr. Alfred Noyes and Messrs. Blackwood Ltd. for 'Forty Singing Seamen', 'Sherwood', and 'The Moon is Up' from *The Collected Poems of Alfred Noyes*.

Mrs. Stephens and Messrs. Macmillan & Co. Ltd. for 'The Snare' and 'The Main-deep' from *Collected Poems* by James Stephens.

Messrs. Sidgwick & Jackson Ltd. for 'Romance' by W. J. Turner.

Mrs. W. B. Yeats, and Messrs. Macmillan & Co. Ltd. for 'The Cat and the Moon' from *The Collected Poems of W. B. Yeats*.

1   *Smells*

WHY is it that the poets tell
So little of the sense of smell?
These are the odours I love well:

The smell of coffee freshly ground;
Or rich plum pudding, holly-crowned;
Or onions fried and deeply browned.

The fragrance of a fumy pipe;
The smell of apples, newly ripe;
And printers' ink on leaden type.

Woods by moonlight in September
Breathe most sweet; and I remember
Many a smoky camp-fire ember.

Camphor, turpentine, and tea,
The balsam of a Christmas tree,
These are whiffs of gramarye . . .
A ship smells best of all to me!

                                C. MORLEY

2   *Sea Fever*

I MUST go down to the seas again, to the lonely sea and the
   sky,
And all I ask is a tall ship and a star to steer her by,
And the wheel's kick and the wind's song and the white sail's
   shaking,
And a grey mist on the sea's face and a grey dawn breaking.

I must go down to the seas again, for the call of the running
   tide
Is a wild call and a clear call that may not be denied;
And all I ask is a windy day with the white clouds flying,
And the flung spray and the blown spume, and the sea-gulls
   crying.

I must go down to the seas again, to the vagrant gipsy life,
To the gull's way and the whale's way where the wind's like a
   whetted knife;
And all I ask is a merry yarn from a laughing fellow-rover,
And quiet sleep and a sweet dream when the long trick's over.

JOHN MASEFIELD

3   *Cargoes*

QUINQUIREME of Nineveh from distant Ophir
Rowing home to haven in sunny Palestine,
      With a cargo of ivory,
      And apes and peacocks,
Sandalwood, cedarwood, and sweet white wine.

Stately Spanish galleon coming from the Isthmus,
Dipping through the Tropics by the palm-green shores,
      With a cargo of diamonds,
      Emeralds, amethysts,
Topazes, and cinnamon, and gold moidores.

Dirty British coaster with a salt-caked smoke stack
Butting through the Channel in the mad March days,
      With a cargo of Tyne coal,
      Road rail, pig-lead,
Firewood, iron-ware, and cheap tin trays.

JOHN MASEFIELD

The Golden Vanity

A SHIP I have got in the North Country
And she goes by the name of the *Golden Vanity*,
O I fear she'll be taken by a Spanish Ga-la-lee,
    As she sails by the Low-lands low.

To the Captain then upspake the little Cabin-boy,
He said, 'What is my fee, if the galley I destroy?
The Spanish Ga-la-lee, if no more it shall annoy,
    As you sail by the Low-lands low.'

'Of silver and of gold I will give you a store;
And my pretty little daughter that dwelleth on the shore,
Of treasure and of fee as well, I'll give to thee galore,
    As we sail by the Low-lands low.'

Then they row'd him up tight in a black bull's skin,
And he held all in his hand an augur sharp and thin,
And he swam until he came to the Spanish Gal-a-lin,
    As she lay by the Low-lands low.

He bored with his augur, he bored once and twice,
And some were playing cards, and some were playing dice,
When the water flowed in it dazzled their eyes,
    And she sank by the Low-lands low.

So the Cabin-boy did swim all to the larboard side,
Saying 'Captain! take me in, I am drifting with the tide!'
'I will shoot you! I will kill you!' the cruel Captain cried,
    'You may sink by the Low-lands low.'

Then the Cabin-boy did swim all to the starboard side,
Saying, 'Messmates, take me in, I am drifting with the tide!'
Then they laid him on the deck, and he closed his eyes and
    died,
    As they sailed by the Low-lands low.

They sew'd his body tight in an old cow's hide,
And they cast the gallant cabin-boy out over the ship side,
And left him without more ado to drift with the tide,
    And to sink by the Low-lands low.

                                  BALLAD

5   *The Owl and the Pussy-cat*

THE Owl and the Pussy-Cat went to sea
    In a beautiful pea-green boat,
They took some honey, and plenty of money,
    Wrapped up in a five-pound note.
The Owl looked up to the stars above,
    And sang to a small guitar,
'O lovely Pussy! O Pussy, my love,
    What a beautiful Pussy you are,
        You are,
        You are!
    What a beautiful Pussy you are!'

Pussy said to the Owl, 'You elegant fowl!
    How charmingly sweet you sing!
O let us be married! too long we have tarried
    But what shall we do for a ring?'
They sailed away for a year and a day,

To the land where the Bong-tree grows,
And there in a wood a Piggy-wig stood,
  With a ring at the end of his nose,
    His nose,
    His nose,
  With a ring at the end of his nose.

'Dear Pig, are you willing to sell for a shilling
  Your ring?' Said the Piggy, 'I will.'
So they took it away, and were married next day
  By the Turkey who lives on the hill.
They dined on mince, and slices of quince,
  Which they ate with a runcible spoon;
And hand in hand, on the edge of the sand,
  They danced by the light of the moon,
    The moon,
    The moon,
  They danced by the light of the moon.

EDWARD LEAR

6   *The Discoverer of the North Cape*

OTHERE, the old sea-captain,
  Who dwelt in Helgoland,
To King Alfred, the Lover of Truth,
Brought a snow-white walrus-tooth,
  Which he held in his brown right hand.

His figure was tall and stately,
  Like a boy's his eye appeared;
His hair was yellow as hay,
But threads of a silvery grey
  Gleamed in his tawny beard.

Hearty and hale was Othere,
  His cheek had the colour of oak;
With a kind of laugh in his speech,
Like the sea-tide on the beach,
  As unto the king he spoke.

And Alfred, King of the Saxons,
  Had a book upon his knees,
And wrote down the wondrous tale
Of him who was first to sail
  Into the Arctic seas.

'So far I live to the northward,
  No man lives north of me;
To the east are wild mountain-chains,
And beyond them meres and plains;
  To the westward all is sea.

'So far I live to the northward,
  From the harbour of Skeringes-hale,
If you only sailed by day,
With a fair wind all the way,
  More than a month would you sail.

'I own six hundred reindeer,
  With sheep and swine beside;
I have tribute from the Finns,
Whalebone and reindeer-skins,
  And ropes of walrus-hide.

'I ploughed the land with horses,
  But my heart was ill at ease,
For the old seafaring men
Came to me now and then,
  With their sagas of the seas:—

'Of Iceland and of Greenland,
  And the stormy Hebrides,
And the undiscovered deep:—
I could not eat or sleep
  For thinking of those seas.

'To the northward stretched the desert,
  How far I fain would know;
So at last I sallied forth,
And three days sailed due north,
  As far as the whale-ships go.

'To the west of me was the ocean,
  To the right the desolate shore,
But I did not slacken sail
For the walrus or the whale,
  Till after three days more.

'The days grew longer and longer,
  Till they became as one,
And southward through the haze
I saw the sullen blaze
  Of the red midnight sun.

'And then uprose before me,
  Upon the water's edge,
The huge and haggard shape
Of that unknown North Cape,
  Whose form is like a wedge.

'The sea was rough and stormy,
  The tempest howled and wailed,
And the sea-fog, like a ghost,
Haunted that dreary coast,
  But onward still I sailed.

'Four days I steered to eastward,
    Four days without a night:
Round in a fiery ring
Went the great sun, O King,
    With red and lurid light.'

Here Alfred, King of the Saxons,
    Ceased writing for a while;
And raised his eyes from his book,
With a strange and puzzled look,
    And an incredulous smile.

But Othere, the old sea-captain,
    He neither paused nor stirred,
Till the King listened, and then
Once more took up his pen,
    And wrote down every word.

'And now the land,' said Othere,
    'Bent southward suddenly,
And I followed the curving shore,
And ever southward bore
    Into a nameless sea.

'And there we hunted the walrus,
    The narwhale and the seal;
Ha! 'twas a noble game!
And like the lightning's flame
    Flew our harpoons of steel.

'There were six of us all together,
    Norsemen of Helgoland;
In two days and no more
We killed of them threescore,
    And dragged them to the strand!'

Here Alfred, the Truth-Teller,
    Suddenly closed his book,
And lifted his blue eyes,
With doubt and strange surmise
    Depicted in their look.

And Othere the old sea-captain
    Stared at him wild and weird,
Then smiled, till his shining teeth
Gleamed white from underneath
    His tawny, quivering beard.

And to the King of the Saxons,
    In witness of the truth,
Raising his noble head,
He stretched his brown hand, and said,
    'Behold this walrus-tooth!'

                    H. W. LONGFELLOW

7   *The Three Fishers*

THREE fishers went sailing away to the West,
    Away to the West as the sun went down;
Each thought on the woman who loved him the best,
    And the children stood watching them out of the town;
For men must work, and women must weep,
And there's little to earn, and many to keep,
    Though the harbour-bar be moaning.

Three wives sat up in the lighthouse tower,
    And trimmed their lamps as the sun went down,
And they looked at the squall, and they looked at the shower,
    And the night-rack came rolling up, ragged and brown;

But men must work, and women must weep,
Though storms be sudden, and waters deep,
  And the harbour-bar be moaning.

Three corpses lay out on the shining sands,
  In the morning gleam as the tide went down,
And the women are weeping and wringing their hands,
  For those who will never come home to the town;
For men must work, and women must weep,
And the sooner it's over, the sooner to sleep,
  And good-bye to the bar and its moaning.

CHARLES KINGSLEY

8   *The Main-deep*

THE long-rólling,
Steady-póuring
Deep-trenchéd
Green billów:

  The wide-topped,
Unbróken,
Green-glacid,
Slow-sliding,

  Cold-flushing,
– On – on – on –
Chill-rushing,
Hush – hushing,

  . . . Hush – hushing . . .
JAMES STEPHENS

In the wild October night-time, when the wind raved
    round the land,
And the Back-sea met the Front-sea, and our doors were
    blocked with sand,
And we heard the drub of Dead-man's Bay, where bones of
    thousands are,
We knew not what the day had done for us at Trafalgar.
                    Had done,
                    Had done,
                For us at Trafalgar!

'Pull hard, and make the Nothe, or down we go!' one says,
    says he.
We pulled; and bedtime brought the storm; but snug at
    home slept we.
Yet all the while our gallants after fighting through the day,
Were beating up and down the dark, sou'-west of Cadiz Bay,
                    The dark,
                    The dark,
                Sou'-west of Cadiz Bay!

The victors and the vanquished then the storm it tossed and
    tore,
As hard they strove, those worn-out men, upon that surly
    shore;
Dead Nelson and his half-dead crew, his foes from near and
    far,
Were rolled together on the deep that night at Trafalgar!
                    The deep,
                    The deep,
                That night at Trafalgar!

                                    THOMAS HARDY

Full Fathom Five

FULL fathom five thy father lies;
   Of his bones are coral made;
Those are pearls that were his eyes:
   Nothing of him that doth fade,
But doth suffer a sea-change
Into something rich and strange.
Sea-nymphs hourly ring his knell:
      Ding-dong.
   Hark! now I hear them—
   Ding-dong, bell!

W. SHAKESPEARE

11 *Epitaph on a Hare*

HERE lies, whom hound did ne'er pursue,
   Nor swifter greyhound follow,
Whose foot ne'er tainted morning dew,
   Nor ear heard huntsman's hallo,

Old Tiney, surliest of his kind
   Who, nursed with tender care,
And to domestic bounds confined,
   Was yet a wild Jack-hare.

Though duly from my hand he took
   His pittance every night,
He did it with a jealous look;
   And, when he could, would bite.

His diet was of wheaten bread,
  And milk, and oats, and straw,
Thistles, or lettuces instead,
  And sand to scour his maw.

On twigs of hawthorn he regaled,
  Or pippins' russet peel;
And, when his juicy salads failed,
  Sliced carrots pleased him well.

A Turkey carpet was his lawn,
  Whereon he loved to bound,
To skip and gambol like a fawn,
  And swing his rump around.

His frisking was at evening hours,
  For then he lost his fear;
But most before approaching showers,
  Or when a storm drew near.

Eight years and five round-rolling moons
  He thus saw steal away,
Dozing out all his idle noons,
  And every night at play.

I kept him for his humour's sake,
  For he would oft beguile
My heart of thoughts that made it ache,
  And force me to a smile.

But now, beneath this walnut shade,
  He finds his long, last home;
And waits in snug concealment laid,
  Till gentler Puss shall come.

He, still more aged, feels the shocks
From which no care can save,
And, partner once of Tiney's box,
Must soon partake his grave.

W. COWPER

12   *The Tale of Custard the Dragon*

BELINDA lived in a little white house,
With a little black kitten and a little gray mouse,
And a little yellow dog and a little red wagon,
And a realio, trulio, little pet dragon.

Now the name of the little black kitten was Ink,
And the little gray mouse, she called her Blink,
And the little yellow dog was sharp as Mustard,
But the dragon was a coward, and she called him Custard.

Custard the dragon had big sharp teeth,
And spikes on top of him and scales underneath,
Mouth like a fireplace, chimney for a nose,
And realio, trulio daggers on his toes.

Belinda was as brave as a barrel full of bears,
And Ink and Blink chased lions down the stairs,
Mustard was as brave as a tiger in a rage,
But Custard cried for a nice safe cage.

Belinda tickled him, she tickled him unmerciful,
Ink, Blink and Mustard they rudely called him Percival,
They all sat laughing in the little red wagon
At the realio, trulio cowardly dragon.

Belinda giggled till she shook the house,
And Blink said Weeck! which is giggling for a mouse,
Ink and Mustard rudely asked his age,
When Custard cried for a nice safe cage.

Suddenly, suddenly they heard a nasty sound,
And Mustard growled, and they all looked around.
Meowch! cried Ink, and Ooh! cried Belinda,
For there was a pirate climbing in the winda.

Pistol in his left hand, pistol in his right,
And he held in his teeth a cutlass bright,
His beard was black, one leg was wood;
It was clear that the pirate meant no good.

Belinda paled, and she cried Help! Help!
But Mustard fled with a terrified yelp,
Ink trickled down to the bottom of the household,
And little mouse Blink strategically mouseholed.

But up jumped Custard, snorting like an engine,
Clashed his tail like irons in a dungeon,
With a clatter and a clank and a jangling squirm
He went at the pirate like a robin at a worm.

The pirate gaped at Belinda's dragon,
And gulped some grog from his pocket flagon,
He fired two bullets, but they didn't hit,
And Custard gobbled him, every bit.

Belinda embraced him, Mustard licked him,
No one mourned for his pirate victim.
Ink and Blink in glee did gyrate
Around the dragon that ate the pyrate.

Belinda still lives in her little white house,
With her little black kitten and her little gray mouse,
And her little yellow dog and her little red wagon,
And her realio, trulio little pet dragon.

Belinda is as brave as a barrel full of bears,
And Ink and Blink chase lions down the stairs.
Mustard is as brave as a tiger in a rage,
But Custard keeps crying for a nice safe cage.

OGDEN NASH

13   *Milk for the Cat*

WHEN the tea is brought at five o'clock,
And all the neat curtains are drawn with care,
The little black cat with bright green eyes
Is suddenly purring there.

At first she pretends, having nothing to do,
She has come in merely to blink by the grate;
But, though tea may be late or the milk may be sour,
She is never late.

And presently her agate eyes
Take a soft large milky haze,
And her independent, casual glance
Becomes a stiff, hard gaze.

Then she stamps her claws or lifts her ears,
Or twists her tail and begins to stir,
Till suddenly all her lithe body becomes
One breathing, trembling purr.

The children eat and wriggle and laugh,
The two old ladies stroke their silk:
But the cat is grown small and thin with desire,
Transformed to a creeping lust for milk.

The white saucer like some full moon descends
At last from the clouds of the table above;
She sighs and dreams and thrills and glows,
Transfigured with love.

She nestles over the shining rim,
Buries her chin in the creamy sea;
Her tail hangs loose; each drowsy paw
Is doubled under each bending knee.

A long, dim ecstasy holds her life;
Her world is an infinite shapeless white,
Till her tongue has curled the last holy drop,
Then she sinks back into the night,

Draws and dips her body to heap
Her sleepy nerves in the great arm-chair,
Lies defeated and buried deep
Three or four hours unconscious there.

HAROLD MONRO

14 *Old Cat Care*

GREEN-EYED Care
May prowl and glare
And poke his snub, be-whiskered nose:
But Door fits tight
Against the Night:
Through criss-cross cracks no evil goes.

Window is small:
No room at all
For Worry and Money, his shoulder-bones:
Chimney is wide,
But Smoke's inside
And happy Smoke would smother his moans.

Be-whiskered Care
May prowl out there:
But I never heard
He caught the Blue Bird.

RICHARD HUGHES

15   *The Cat and the Moon*

THE cat went here and there
And the moon spun round like a top,
And the nearest kin of the moon,
The creeping cat, looked up.
Black Minnaloushe stared at the moon,
For wander and wail as he would,
The pure cold light in the sky
Troubled his animal blood.
Minnaloushe runs in the grass
Lifting his delicate feet.
Do you dance, Minnaloushe, do you dance?
When two close kindred meet
What better than call a dance?
Maybe the moon may learn,
Tired of that courtly fashion,
A new dance turn.

Minnaloushe creeps through the grass
From moonlit place to place.
The sacred moon overhead
Has taken a new phase.
Does Minnaloushe know that his pupils
Will pass from change to change,
And that from round to crescent,
From crescent to round they range?
Minnaloushe creeps through the grass
Alone, important and wise,
And lifts to the changing moon
His changing eyes.

W. B. YEATS

16 *Silver*

SLOWLY, silently, now the moon
Walks the night in her silver shoon;
This way, and that, she peers, and sees
Silver fruit upon silver trees;
One by one the casements catch
Her beams beneath the silvery thatch;
Couched in his kennel, like a log,
With paws of silver sleeps the dog;
From their shadowy cote the white breasts peep
Of doves in a silver-feathered sleep;
A harvest mouse goes scampering by,
With silver claws, and silver eye;
And moveless fish in the water gleam,
By silver reeds in a silver stream.

WALTER DE LA MARE

WHENEVER the moon and stars are set,
    Whenever the wind is high,
All night long in the dark and wet,
    A man goes riding by.
Late in the night when the fires are out,
Why does he gallop and gallop about?

Whenever the trees are crying aloud,
    And ships are tossed at sea,
By, on the highway, low and loud,
    By at the gallop goes he.
By at the gallop he goes, and then
By he comes back at the gallop again.

R. L. STEVENSON

THE moon is up: the stars are bright:
    The wind is fresh and free!
We're out to seek for gold to-night
    Across the silver sea!
The world is growing grey and old:
    Break out the sails again!
We're out to seek a Realm of Gold
    Beyond the Spanish Main.

We're sick of all the cringing knees,
    The courtly smiles and lies!
God, let thy singing Channel breeze
    Lighten our hearts and eyes!

Let love no more be bought and sold
    For earthly loss or gain;
We're out to seek an Age of Gold
    Beyond the Spanish Main.

Beyond the light of far Cathay,
    Beyond all mortal dreams,
Beyond the reach of night and day
    Our El Dorado gleams,
Revealing—as the skies unfold—
    A star without a stain,
The Glory of the Gates of Gold
    Beyond the Spanish Main.

ALFRED NOYES

19 *Matin Song*

PACK, clouds, away! and welcome, day!
    With night we banish sorrow.
Sweet air, blow soft; mount, lark, aloft
    To give my Love good-morrow!
Wings from the wind to please her mind,
    Notes from the lark I'll borrow:
Bird, prune thy wing! nightingale, sing!
    To give my Love good-morrow!
      To give my Love good-morrow
      Notes from them all I'll borrow.

Wake from thy nest, robin redbreast!
    Sing, birds, in every furrow!
And from each bill let music shrill
    Give my fair Love good-morrow!

Blackbird and thrush in every bush,
    Stare, linnet, and cocksparrow,
You pretty elves, among yourselves
    Sing my fair Love good-morrow!
        To give my Love good-morrow!
        Sing, birds, in every furrow!

T. HEYWOOD

The Throstle

'SUMMER is coming, summer is coming.
    I know it, I know it, I know it.
Light again, leaf again, life again, love again,'
    Yes, my wild little Poet.

Sing the new year in under the blue.
    Last year you sang it as gladly.
'New, new, new, new'! Is it then so new
    That you should carol so madly?

'Love again, song again, nest again, young again,'
    Never a prophet so crazy!
And hardly a daisy as yet, little friend,
    See, there is hardly a daisy.

'Here again, here, here, here, happy year!'
    O warble unchidden, unbidden!
Summer is coming, is coming, my dear,
    And all the winters are hidden.

LORD TENNYSON

21 *The Eagle*

HE clasps the crag with crooked hands;
Close to the sun in lonely lands,
Ring'd with the azure world, he stands.

The wrinkled sea beneath him crawls;
He watches from his mountain walls,
And like a thunderbolt he falls.

LORD TENNYSON

22 *The Jackdaw of Rheims*

THE Jackdaw sat on the Cardinal's chair!
  Bishop and abbot and prior were there;
  Many a monk and many a friar,
  Many a knight and many a squire,
With a great many more of lesser degree—
In sooth a goodly company;
And they served the Lord Primate on bended knee.
  Never, I ween, was a prouder seen,
Read of in books, or dreamt of in dreams,
Than the Cardinal Lord Archbishop of Rheims!

In and out through the motley rout,
That little Jackdaw kept hopping about;
  Here and there, like a dog in a fair,
  Over comfits and cates, and dishes and plates,
Cowl and cope, and rochet and pall,
Mitre and crosier—he hopp'd upon all!
  With saucy air, he perch'd on the chair
Where, in state, the great Lord Cardinal sat
In the great Lord Cardinal's great red hat;
  And he peer'd in the face of his Lordship's Grace,

With a satisfied look, as if he would say,
'We two are the greatest folks here to-day!'
And the priests, with awe, as such freaks they saw,
Said, 'The Devil must be in that little Jackdaw!'

The feast was over, the board was clear'd,
The flawns and the custards had all disappear'd,
And six little Singing-Boys—dear little souls!
In nice clean faces, and nice white stoles,
Came, in order due, two by two,
Marching that grand refectory through!
A nice little boy held a golden ewer,
Emboss'd and fill'd with water, as pure
As any that flows between Rheims and Namur,
Which a nice little boy stood ready to catch
In a fine golden hand-basin made to match.
Two nice little boys, rather more grown,
Carried lavender-water and eau de Cologne,
And a nice little boy had a nice cake of soap,
Worthy of washing the hands of the Pope.
One little boy more a napkin bore,
Of the best white diaper, fringed with pink,
And a Cardinal's hat mark'd in 'permanent ink'.
The great Lord Cardinal turns at the sight
Of these nice little boys dress'd all in white;
From his finger he draws his costly turquoise,
And, not thinking at all about little Jackdaws,
Deposits it straight by the side of his plate,
While the nice little boys on his Eminence wait;
Till, when nobody's dreaming of any such thing,
That little Jackdaw hops off with the ring!

There's a cry and a shout, and a deuce of a rout,
And nobody seems to know what they're about,

But the Monks have their pockets all turn'd inside out;
   The Friars are kneeling, and hunting, and feeling
The carpet, the floor, and the walls, and the ceiling.
   The Cardinal drew off each plum-colour'd shoe,
And left his red stockings exposed to the view;
   He peeps and he feels in the toes and the heels;
They turn up the dishes—they turn up the plates—
They take up the poker and poke out the grates,
   They turn up the rugs, they examine the mugs—
   But no!—no such thing;—they can't find the ring!
And the Abbot declared that, 'when nobody twigg'd it,
Some rascal or other had popp'd in, and prigg'd it!'

The Cardinal rose with a dignified look;
He call'd for his candle, his bell, and his book!
   In holy anger, and pious grief,
   He solemnly cursed that rascally thief!
   He cursed him at board, he cursed him in bed;
   From the sole of his foot to the crown of his head;
   He cursed him in sleeping, that every night
   He should dream of the Devil, and wake in a fright;
   He cursed him in eating, he cursed him in drinking;
   He cursed him in coughing, in sneezing, in winking;
   He cursed him in sitting, in standing, in lying;
   He cursed him in walking, in riding, in flying;
   He cursed him in living, he cursed him dying!—
Never was heard such a terrible curse!
   But what gave rise to no little surprise,
Nobody seem'd one penny the worse!

   The day was gone, the night came on,
The Monks and the Friars they search'd till dawn;
   When the Sacristan saw, on crumpled claw,
Come limping a poor little lame Jackdaw;
   No longer gay, as on yesterday;

His feathers all seem'd to be turn'd the wrong way;
His pinions droop'd; he could hardly stand;
His head was as bald as the palm of your hand;
    His eye so dim, so wasted each limb,
That, heedless of grammar, they all cried, 'That's him!
That's the scamp that has done this scandalous thing!
That's the thief that has got my Lord Cardinal's ring!'

The poor little Jackdaw, when the Monks he saw,
Feebly gave vent to the ghost of a caw;
And turn'd his bald head, as much as to say:
'Pray be so good as to walk this way!'
    Slower and slower he limped on before,
Till they came to the back of the belfry door,
    When the first thing they saw, midst the sticks and the
        straw,
Was the ring in the nest of that little Jackdaw!

Then the great Lord Cardinal call'd for his book,
And off that terrible curse he took;
    —When those words were heard, that poor little bird
Was so changed in a moment, 'twas really absurd.
    He grew sleek and fat; in addition to that,
A fresh crop of feathers came thick as a mat!

His tail waggled more even than before;
But no longer it wagged with an impudent air,
No longer he perch'd on the Cardinal's chair.
    He hopp'd now about with a gait devout;
At Matins, at Vespers, he never was out;
And, so far from any more pilfering deeds,
He always seem'd telling the Confessor's beads.
If any one lied—or if any one swore—
Or slumber'd in prayer-time and happen'd to snore,
    That good Jackdaw would give a great 'Caw!'

34

As much as to say, 'Don't do so any more!'
While many remark'd as his manners they saw,
That they 'never had known such a pious Jackdaw!'

He long lived the pride of that country side,
And at last in the odour of sanctity died;
When, as words were too faint his merits to paint,
The Conclave determined to make him a Saint!
And on newly-made Saints and Popes, as you know,
It's the custom, at Rome, new names to bestow,
So they canonized him by the name of Jim Crow!

R. H. BARHAM

23 *The Wraggle-Taggle Gipsies, O*

THREE gipsies stood at the castle gate,
 They sang so high, they sang so low,
They sang so shrill, they sang so sweet,
 Her heart it melted away like snow.

They sang so sweet, they sang so shrill,
 That fast her tears began to flow,
And she pulled off her silken gown
 To go with the wraggle-taggle gipsies, O.

She pluckèd off her high-heeled shoes,
 Her golden rings and all her show;
She would in the street, with her bare, bare feet,
 All out in the wind and the weather, O.

'O saddle to me my milk-white steed,
 Go fetch your lord his pony, O!
That he may ride and seek his bride,
 Who is gone with the wraggle-taggle gipsies, O!'

O he rode high, and he rode low,
  He rode through wood and copses too,
Until he came to an open field,
  And there he espied his lady, O.

'What makes you leave your house and land?
  Your golden treasures to forego?
What makes you leave your new-wedded lord,
  To follow the wraggle-taggle gipsies, O?'

'What care I for my house and land?
  What care I for my treasure, O?
What care I for my new-wedded lord?
  I'm off with the wraggle-taggle gipsies, O!'

'Last night you slept on a goose-feather bed,
  With the sheet turned down so bravely, O!
And to-night you'll sleep in a cold open field,
  Along with the wraggle-taggle gipsies, O!'

'What care I for a goose-feather bed,
  With the sheet turned down so bravely, O!
For to-night I shall sleep in a cold open field,
  Along with the wraggle-taggle gipsies, O!'

OLD SONG

GIVE to me the life I love,
  Let the lave go by me,
Give the jolly heaven above
  And the by-way nigh me.
Bed in the bush with stars to see,
  Bread I dip in the river—
There's the life for a man like me,
  There's the life for ever.

Let the blow fall soon or late,
  Let what will be o'er me:
Give the face of earth around
  And the road before me.
Wealth I seek not, hope nor love,
  Nor a friend to know me;
All I seek, the heaven above
  And the road below me.

Or let Autumn fall on me
  Where afield I linger,
Silencing the bird on tree,
  Biting the blue finger:
White as meal the frosty field—
  Warm the fireside haven—
Not to Autumn will I yield,
  Not to Winter even!

Let the blow fall soon or late,
  Let what will be o'er me;
Give the face of earth around,
  And the road before me.

37

Wealth I ask not, hope nor love,
　　Nor a friend to know me;
All I ask, the heaven above,
　　And the road below me.

R. L. STEVENSON

Over the Sea to Skye

SING me a song of a lad that is gone,
　　Say, could that lad be I?
Merry of soul he sailed on a day
　　Over the sea to Skye.

Mull was astern, Rum on the port,
　　Eigg on the starboard bow;
Glory of youth glowed in his soul:
　　Where is that glory now?

Sing me a song of a lad that is gone,
　　Say, could that lad be I?
Merry of soul he sailed on a day
　　Over the sea to Skye.

Give me again all that was there,
　　Give me the sun that shone!
Give me the eyes, give me the soul,
　　Give me the lad that's gone!

Sing me a song of a lad that is gone,
　　Say, could that lad be I?
Merry of soul he sailed on a day
　　Over the sea to Skye.

Billow and breeze, islands and seas,
Mountains of rain and sun,
All that was good, all that was fair,
All that was me is gone.

R. L. STEVENSON

26   *John Anderson, My Jo*

JOHN ANDERSON, my jo, John,
When we were first acquent,
Your locks were like the raven,
Your bonny brow was brent;
But now your brow is beld, John,
Your locks are like the snow;
But blessings on your frosty pow,
John Anderson, my jo.

John Anderson, my jo, John,
We clamb the hill thegither;
And mony a cantie day, John,
We've had wi' ane anither:
Now we maun totter down, John,
And hand in hand we'll go,
And sleep thegither at the foot,
John Anderson, my jo.

ROBERT BURNS

jo, sweetheart.   *brent*, smooth, unwrinkled.   *pow*, head.
cantie, happy.

HE cut a sappy sucker from the muckle rodden-tree,
He trimmed it, an' he wet it, an' he thumped it on his
    knee;
He never heard the teuchat when the harrow broke her eggs,
He missed the craggit heron nabbin' puddocks in the seggs,
He forgot to hound the collie at the cattle when they
    strayed,
But you should hae seen the whistle that the wee herd
    made!

He wheepled on't at mornin' an' he tweetled on't at nicht,
He puffed his freckled cheeks until his nose sank oot o' sicht.
The kye were late for milkin' when he piped them up the
    closs,
The kitlins got his supper syne, an' he was beddit boss;
But he cared na doit nor docken what they did or thocht or
    said,
There was comfort in the whistle that the wee herd made.

For lyin' lang o' mornin's he had clawed the caup for weeks,
But noo he had his bonnet on afore the lave had breeks;
He was whistlin' to the porridge that were hott'rin' on the
    fire,
He was whistlin' owre the travise to the baillie in the byre;
Nae a blackbird nor a mavis that hae pipin' for their trade
Was a marrow for the whistle that the wee herd made.

rodden, rowan.   *teuchat*, peewit.   *craggit*, long-necked.
boss, empty.   *clawed the caup*, scraped the basin.   *travise*,
                 partition.

He played a march to battle, it cam' dirlin' through the
    mist,
Till the halflin' squared his shou'ders an' made up his mind
    to 'list;
He tried a spring for wooers, though he wistna what it
    meant,
But the kitchen-lass was lauchin' an' he thocht she maybe
    kent;
He got ream an' buttered bannocks for the loving lilt he
    played.
Wasna that a cheery whistle that the wee herd made?

He blew them rants sae lively, schottisches, reels an' jigs,
The foalie flung his muckle legs an' capered owre the rigs.
The grey-tailed futt'rat bobbit oot to hear his ain strathspey,
The bawd cam' loupin' through the corn to 'Clean Pease
    Strae.'
The feet o' ilka man an' beast gat youkie when he played—
Hae ye ever heard o' whistle like the wee herd made?

But the snaw it stopped the herdin', an' the winter brocht
    him dool,
When in spite o' hacks an' chilblains he was shod again for
    school;
He couldna sough the catechis nor pipe the rule o' three,
He was keepit in an' lickit when the ither loons got free;
But he aften played the truant—'twas the only thing he
    played,
For the maister brunt the whistle that the wee herd made!

C. MURRAY

ream, cream.   *futt'rat*, weasel.   *bawd*, hare.   *youkie*,
    restless.

I REMEMBER, I remember,
The house where I was born,
The little window where the sun
Came peeping in at morn;
He never came a wink too soon
Nor brought too long a day;
But now, I often wish the night
Had borne my breath away!

I remember, I remember,
The roses, red and white,
The violets, and the lily-cups,
Those flowers made of light!
The lilacs where the robin built,
And where my brother set
The laburnum on his birth-day,—
The tree is living yet!

I remember, I remember,
Where I was used to swing,
And thought the air must rush as fresh
To swallows on the wing;
My spirit flew in feathers then,
That is so heavy now,
And summer pools could hardly cool
The fever on my brow!

I remember, I remember,
The fir trees dark and high;
I used to think their slender tops
Were close against the sky:

42

It was a childish ignorance,
But now 'tis little joy
To know I'm farther off from Heaven
Than when I was a boy.

T. HOOD

29   *Remember now thy Creator*

REMEMBER now thy Creator in the days of thy youth, while the evil days come not, nor the years draw nigh, when thou shalt say, I have no pleasure in them;

While the sun, or the light, or the moon, or the stars, be not darkened, nor the clouds return after the rain:

In the day when the keepers of the house shall tremble, and the strong men shall bow themselves, and the grinders cease because they are few, and those that look out of the windows be darkened,

And the doors shall be shut in the streets, when the sound of the grinding is low, and he shall rise up at the voice of the bird, and all the daughters of musick shall be brought low;

Also when they shall be afraid of that which is high, and fears shall be in the way, and the almond tree shall flourish, and the grasshopper shall be a burden, and desire shall fail: because man goeth to his long home, and the mourners go about the streets:

Or ever the silver cord be loosed, or the golden bowl be broken, or the pitcher be broken at the fountain, or the wheel broken at the cistern.

Then shall the dust return to the earth as it was: and the spirit shall return to God who gave it.

THE BIBLE

WHEN I was but thirteen or so
  I went into a golden land,
Chimborazo, Cotopaxi
  Took me by the hand.

My father died, my brother too,
  They passed like fleeting dreams,
I stood where Popocatapetl
  In the sunlight gleams.

I dimly heard the master's voice
  And boys far-off at play,
Chimborazo, Cotopaxi
  Had stolen me away.

I walked in a great golden dream
  To and fro from school—
Shining Popocatapetl
  The dusty streets did rule.

I walked home with a gold dark boy,
  And never a word I'd say,
Chimborazo, Cotopaxi
  Had taken my speech away:

I gazed entranced upon his face
  Fairer than any flower—
O shining Popocatapetl,
  It was thy magic hour:

The houses, people, traffic seemed
  Thin fading dreams by day,
Chimborazo, Cotopaxi
  They had stolen my soul away!

                                    W. J. TURNER

IF I were Lord of Tartary,
  Myself, and me alone,
My bed should be of ivory,
  Of beaten gold my throne;
And in my court should peacocks flaunt,
And in my forests tigers haunt,
And in my pools great fishes slant
  Their fins athwart the sun.

If I were Lord of Tartary,
  Trumpeters every day
To every meal should summon me,
  And in my courtyards bray;
And in the evenings lamps should shine,
Yellow as honey, red as wine,
While harp, and flute, and mandoline
  Made music sweet and gay.

If I were Lord of Tartary,
  I'd wear a robe of beads,
White, and gold, and green they'd be—
  And small and thick as seeds;
And ere should wane the morning-star,
I'd don my robe and scimitar,
And zebras seven should draw my car
  Through Tartary's dark glades.

Lord of the fruits of Tartary,
  Her rivers silver-pale!
Lord of the hills of Tartary,
  Glen, thicket, wood and dale!

Her flashing stars, her scented breeze,
Her trembling lakes, like foamless seas,
Her bird-delighting citron-trees,
    In every purple vale!

WALTER DE LA MARE

32 *Forty Singing Seamen*

ACROSS the seas of Wonderland to Mogadore we plodded,
  Forty singing seamen in an old black barque,
And we landed in the twilight where a Polyphemus nodded
  With his battered moon-eye winking red and yellow
        through the dark!
      For his eye was growing mellow,
      Rich and ripe and red and yellow,
  As was time, since old Ulysses made him bellow in the
        dark!
CHORUS—Since Ulysses bunged his eye up with a pine-
      torch in the dark!

Were they mountains in the gloaming or the giant's ugly
      shoulders
  Just beneath the rolling eyeball, with its bleared and
      vinous glow,
Red and yellow o'er the purple of the pines among the
      boulders
  And the shaggy horror brooding on the sullen slopes below,
      Were they pines among the boulders
      Or the hair upon his shoulders?
  We were only simple seamen, so of course we didn't
      know.
CHORUS—We were simple singing seamen, so of course we
      couldn't know.

46

But we crossed a plain of poppies, and we came upon a foun-
tain
  Not of water, but of jewels, like a spray of leaping fire;
And behind it, in an emerald glade, beneath a golden moun-
tain
  There stood a crystal palace, for a sailor to admire;
    For a troop of ghosts came round us,
    Which with leaves of bay they crowned us,
  Then with grog they wellnigh drowned us, to the depth of
our desire!
CHORUS—And 'twas very friendly of them, as a sailor can
admire!

There was music all about us, we were growing quite forget-
ful
  We were only singing seamen from the dirt of London-
town,
Though the nectar that we swallowed seemed to vanish half
regretful
  As if we wasn't good enough to take such vittles down,
    When we saw a sudden figure,
    Tall and black as any nigger,
  Like the devil—only bigger—drawing near us with a
frown!
CHORUS—Like the devil—but much bigger—and he wore
a golden crown!

And 'What's all this?' he growls at us! With dignity we
chaunted,
  'Forty singing seamen, sir, as won't be put upon!'
'What? Englishmen?' he cries, 'Well, if ye don't mind being
haunted,
  Faith you're welcome to my palace; I'm the famous
Prester John!

47

Will ye walk into my palace?
I don't bear 'ee any malice!
One and all ye shall be welcome in the halls of Prester John!'
CHORUS—So we walked into the palace and the halls of
Prester John!

Now the door was one great diamond and the hall a hollow
ruby—
Big as Beachy Head, my lads, nay bigger by a half!
And I sees the mate wi' mouth agape, a-staring like a booby,
And the skipper close behind him, with his tongue out like
a calf!
Now the way to take it rightly
Was to walk along politely
Just as if you didn't notice—so I couldn't help but laugh!
CHORUS—For they both forgot their manners and the crew
was bound to laugh!

But he took us through his palace and, my lads, as I'm a sinner,
We walked into an opal like a sunset-coloured cloud—
'My dining-room,' he says, and, quick as light we saw a dinner
Spread before us by the fingers of a hidden fairy crowd;
And the skipper, swaying gently
After dinner, murmurs faintly,
'I looks to-wards you, Prester John, you've done us very
proud!'
CHORUS—And we drank his health with honours, for he
done us *very* proud!

Then he walks us to his garden where we sees a feathered
demon
Very splendid and important on a sort of spicy tree!
'That's the Phoenix,' whispers Prester, 'which all eddicated
seamen

48

Knows the only one existent, and *he's* waiting for to flee!
　　When his hundred years expire
　　Then he'll set hisself afire
And another from his ashes rise most beautiful to see!'
CHORUS—With wings of rose and emerald most beautiful
　　to see!

Then he says, 'In yonder forest there's a little silver river,
　　And whosoever drinks of it, his youth shall never die!
The centuries go by, but Prester John endures for ever
　　With his music in the mountains and his magic on the sky!
　　While *your* hearts are growing colder,
　　While your world is growing older,
　　There's a magic in the distance, where the sea-line meets
　　the sky.'
CHORUS—It shall call to singing seamen till the fount o'
　　song is dry!

So we thought we'd up and seek it, but that forest fair
　　defied us—
First a crimson leopard laughs at us most horrible to see,
Then a sea-green lion came and sniffed and licked his chops
　　and eyed us,
　　While a red and yellow unicorn was dancing round a tree!
　　We was trying to look thinner,
　　Which was hard, because our dinner
　　Must ha' made us very tempting to a cat o' high degree!
CHORUS—Must ha' made us very tempting to the whole
　　menarjeree!

So we scuttled from that forest and across the poppy
　　meadows
　　Where the awful shaggy horror brooded o'er us in the
　　dark!

And we pushes out from shore again a-jumping at our
        shadows,
  And pulls away most joyful to the old black barque!
        And home again we plodded
        While the Polyphemus nodded
  With his battered moon-eye winking red and yellow
        through the dark.
CHORUS—Oh, the moon above the mountains, red and
        yellow through the dark!

Across the seas of Wonderland to London-town we blun-
        dered,
  Forty singing seamen as was puzzled for to know
If the visions that we saw was caused by—here again we
        pondered—
    A tipple in a vision forty thousand years ago.
        Could the grog we *dreampt* we swallowed
        Make us *dream* of all that followed?
  We were only simple seamen, so of course we didn't know!
CHORUS—We were simple singing seamen, so of course we
        could not know!

ALFRED NOYES

33   *The Song of the Cyclops*

BRAVE iron, brave hammer, from your sound
The art of music has her ground:
On the anvil thou keep'st time,
Thy knick-a-knock is a smith's best chime.
    Yet thwick-a-thwack, thwick, thwack-a-thwack, thwack,
    Make our brawny sinews crack:
    Then pit-a-pat, pat, pit-a-pat, pat,
    Till thickest bars be beaten flat.

We shoe the horses of the sun,
Harness the dragons of the moon;
Forge Cupid's quiver, bow, and arrows,
And our dame's coach that's drawn with sparrows.
   Till thwick-a-thwack, &c.

Jove's roaring cannons and his rammers
We beat out with our Lemnian hammers;
Mars his gauntlet, helm, and spear,
And Gorgon shield are all made here.
   Till thwick-a-thwack, &c.

The grate which, shut, the day outbars,
Those golden studs, which nail the stars,
The globe's case and the axle-tree,
Who can hammer these but we?
   Till thwick-a-thwack, &c.

A warming-pan to heat earth's bed,
Lying i' the frozen zone half-dead;
Hob-nails to serve the man i' the moon,
And sparrowbills to clout Pan's shoon,
   Whose work but ours?
   Till thwick-a-thwack, &c.

Venus' kettles, pots, and pans
We make, or else she brawls and bans;
Tongs, shovels, and irons have their places,
Else she scratches all our faces.
   Till thwick-a-thwack, thwick, thwack-a-thwack,
     thwack,
   Make our brawny sinews crack:
   Then pit-a-pat, pat, pit-a-pat, pat,
   Till thickest bars be beaten flat.

T. DEKKER

The Bells

HEAR the sledges with the bells—
          Silver bells!
What a world of merriment their melody foretells!
        How they tinkle, tinkle, tinkle,
            In the icy air of night!
        While the stars, that oversprinkle
        All the heavens, seem to twinkle
            With a crystalline delight;
          Keeping time, time, time,
          In a sort of Runic rhyme,
To the tintinnabulation that so musically wells
      From the bells, bells, bells, bells,
            Bells, bells, bells—
  From the jingling and the tinkling of the bells.

        Hear the mellow wedding bells,
            Golden bells!
What a world of happiness their harmony foretells!
        Through the balmy air of night
        How they ring out their delight!
          From the molten golden-notes,
            And all in tune,
        What a liquid ditty floats
  To the turtle-dove that listens, while she gloats
            On the moon!
      Oh, from out the sounding cells,
What a gush of euphony voluminously wells!
            How it swells!
            How it dwells
        On the future! how it tells
        Of the rapture that impels

To the swinging and the ringing
  Of the bells, bells, bells,
 Of the bells, bells, bells, bells,
    Bells, bells, bells—
To the rhyming and the chiming of the bells!

   Hear the loud alarum bells—
      Brazen bells!
What a tale of terror now their turbulency tells!
   In the startled ear of night
   How they scream out their affright!
    Too much horrified to speak,
    They can only shriek, shriek,
       Out of tune,
In a clamorous appealing to the mercy of the fire,
In a mad expostulation with the deaf and frantic fire
    Leaping higher, higher, higher,
    In a desperate desire,
    And a resolute endeavour
    Now—now to sit or never,
By the side of the pale-faced moon.
    Oh, the bells, bells, bells!
    What a tale their terror tells
       Of Despair!
   How they clang, and clash, and roar!
   What a horror they outpour
On the bosom of the palpitating air!
    Yet the ear it fully knows,
       By the twanging,
       And the clanging,
    How the danger ebbs and flows;
   Yet the ear distinctly tells,
       In the jangling,
       And the wrangling,

How the danger sinks and swells,
By the sinking or the swelling in the anger of the bells—
Of the bells—
Of the bells, bells, bells, bells,
Bells, bells, bells—
In the clamour and the clangour of the bells!

·Hear the tolling of the bells—
Iron bells!
What a world of solemn thought their monody compels
In the silence of the night,
How we shiver with affright
At the melancholy menace of their tone!
For every sound that floats
From the rust within their throats
Is a groan.
And the people—ah, the people—
They that dwell up in the steeple,
All alone,
And who tolling, tolling, tolling,
In that muffled monotone,
Feel a glory in so rolling
On the human heart a stone—
They are neither man nor woman—
They are neither brute nor human—
They are Ghouls:
And their king it is who tolls;
And he rolls, rolls, rolls,
Rolls
A paean from the bells!
And his merry bosom swells
With the paean of the bells!
And he dances, and he yells;
Keeping time, time, time,

In a sort of Runic rhyme,
    To the paean of the bells—
        Of the bells:
Keeping time, time, time,
In a sort of Runic rhyme,
    To the throbbing of the bells—
Of the bells, bells, bells—
    To the sobbing of the bells,
Keeping time, time, time,
    As he knells, knells, knells,
In a happy Runic rhyme,
    To the rolling of the bells—
Of the bells, bells, bells—
    To the tolling of the bells,
Of the bells, bells, bells, bells,
        Bells, bells, bells—
To the moaning and the groaning of the bells.

                                    E. A. POE

35   *The Bells of Heaven*

'TWOULD ring the bells of Heaven
    The wildest peal for years,
If Parson lost his senses
    And people came to theirs,
And he and they together
    Knelt down with angry prayers
For tamed and shabby tigers,
    And dancing dogs and bears,
And wretched, blind pit ponies,
    And little hunted hares.

                    RALPH HODGSON

The Snare

I HEAR a sudden cry of pain!
　　There is a rabbit in a snare:
Now I hear the cry again,
　　But I cannot tell from where.

But I cannot tell from where
　　He is calling out for aid;
Crying on the frightened air,
　　Making everything afraid.

Making everything afraid,
　　Wrinkling up his little face,
As he cries again for aid;
　　And I cannot find the place!

And I cannot find the place
　　Where his paw is in the snare:
Little one! Oh, little one!
　　I am searching everywhere.

JAMES STEPHENS

The Donkey

WHEN fishes flew and forests walked
　　And figs grew upon thorn,
Some moment when the moon was blood
　　Then surely I was born;

With monstrous head and sickening cry
　　And ears like errant wings,
The devil's walking parody
　　On all four-footed things.

The tattered outlaw of the earth,
    Of ancient crooked will:
Starve, scourge, deride me: I am dumb,
    I keep my secret still.

Fools! For I also had my hour;
    One far fierce hour and sweet:
There was a shout about my ears,
    And palms before my feet.

G. K. CHESTERTON

38   The Law of the Jungle

Now this is the Law of the Jungle—as old and as true as the sky;
And the Wolf that shall keep it may prosper, but the Wolf that shall
*   break it must die.*

As the creeper that girdles the tree-trunk the Law runneth forward and
*   back—*
For the strength of the Pack is the Wolf, and the strength of the Wolf
*   is the Pack.*

Wash daily from nose-tip to tail-tip; drink deeply, but never
    too deep;
And remember the night is for hunting, and forget not the
    day is for sleep.

The Jackal may follow the Tiger, but, Cub, when thy
    whiskers are grown,
Remember the Wolf is a hunter—go forth and get food of
    thine own.

Keep peace with the Lords of the Jungle—the Tiger, the
    Panther, the Bear;
And trouble not Hathi the Silent, and mock not the Boar in
    his lair.

When Pack meets with Pack in the Jungle, and neither will
    go from the trail,
Lie down till the leaders have spoken—it may be fair words
    shall prevail.

When ye fight with a Wolf of the Pack, ye must fight him
    alone and afar,
Lest others take part in the quarrel, and the Pack be dimin-
    ished by war.

The Lair of the Wolf is his refuge, and where he has made
    him his home,
Not even the Head Wolf may enter, not even the Council
    may come.

The Lair of the Wolf is his refuge, but where he has digged
    it too plain,
The Council shall send him a message, and so he shall change
    it again.

If ye kill before midnight, be silent, and wake not the woods
    with your bay,
Lest ye frighten the deer from the crops, and the brothers go
    empty away.

Ye may kill for yourselves, and your mates, and your cubs
    as they need, and ye can;
But kill not for pleasure of killing, and *seven times never kill
    Man!*

If ye plunder his Kill from a weaker, devour not all in thy
    pride;
Pack-Right is the right of the meanest; so leave him the
    head and the hide.

The Kill of the Pack is the meat of the Pack. Ye must eat
    where it lies;
And no one may carry away of that meat to his lair, or he
    dies.

The Kill of the Wolf is the meat of the Wolf. He may do
    what he will,
But, till he has given permission, the Pack may not eat of
    that Kill.

Cub-Right is the right of the Yearling. From all of his Pack
    he may claim
Full-gorge when the killer has eaten; and none may refuse
    him the same.

Lair-Right is the right of the Mother. From all of her year
    she may claim
One haunch of each kill for her litter; and none may deny
    her the same.

Cave-Right is the right of the Father—to hunt by himself for
    his own:
He is freed of all calls to the Pack; he is judged by the
    Council alone.

Because of his age and his cunning, because of his gripe and
    his paw,
In all that the Law leaveth open, the word of the Head Wolf
    is Law.

Now these are the Laws of the Jungle, and many and mighty are
    they;
But the head and the hoof of the Law and the haunch and the hump is
    —Obey!

RUDYARD KIPLING

39   *The Little Dog's Day*

ALL in the town were still asleep,
When the sun came up with a shout and a leap.
In the lonely streets unseen by man,
A little dog danced. And the day began.

All his life he'd been good, as far as he could,
And the poor little beast had done all that he should.
But this morning he swore, by Odin and Thor
And the Canine Valhalla—he'd stand it no more!

So his prayer he got granted—to do just what he wanted,
Prevented by none, for the space of a day.
'Jam incipiebo,[1] sedere facebo,'[2]
In dog-Latin he quoth, 'Euge! sophos! hurray!'

He fought with the he-dogs, and winked at the she-dogs,
A thing that had never been *heard* of before.
'For the stigma of gluttony, I care not a button!' he
Cried, and ate all he could swallow—and more.

He took sinewy lumps from the shins of old frumps,
And mangled the errand-boys—when he could get 'em.
He shammed furious *rabies*, and bit all the babies,
And followed the cats up the trees, and then ate 'em!

[1] Now we're off.   [2] I'll make them sit up.

60

They thought 'twas the devil was holding a revel,
And sent for the parson to drive him away;
For the town never knew such a hullabaloo
As that little dog raised—till the end of that day.

When the blood-red sun had gone burning down,
And the lights were lit in the little town,
Outside, in the gloom of the twilight grey,
The little dog died when he'd had his day.

RUPERT BROOKE

40　*The Pied Piper of Hamelin*

I

HAMELIN town's in Brunswick,
　By famous Hanover city;
The river Weser, deep and wide,
Washes its wall on the southern side;
A pleasanter spot you never spied;
　But, when begins my ditty,
Almost five hundred years ago,
To see the townsfolk suffer so
　From vermin, was a pity.

II

Rats!
They fought the dogs and killed the cats,
　And bit the babies in the cradles,
And ate the cheeses out of the vats,
　And licked the soup from the cooks' own ladles,
Split open the kegs of salted sprats,
Made nests inside men's Sunday hats,

And even spoiled the women's chats
    By drowning their speaking
    With shrieking and squeaking
In fifty different sharps and flats.

III

At last the people in a body
    To the Town Hall came flocking:
"Tis clear,' cried they, 'our Mayor's a noddy;
    And as for our Corporation—shocking
To think we buy gowns lined with ermine
For dolts that can't or won't determine
What's best to rid us of our vermin!
You hope, because you're old and obese,
To find in the furry civic robe ease?
Rouse up, sirs! Give your brains a racking
To find the remedy we're lacking,
Or, sure as fate, we'll send you packing!'
At this the Mayor and Corporation
Quaked with a mighty consternation.

IV

An hour they sat in council,
    At length the Mayor broke silence:
'For a guilder I'd my ermine gown sell,
    I wish I were a mile hence!
It's easy to bid one rack one's brain—
I'm sure my poor head aches again,
I've scratched it so, and all in vain.
Oh for a trap, a trap, a trap!'
Just as he said this, what should hap
At the chamber door but a gentle tap?
'Bless us,' cries the Mayor, 'what's that?'

(With the Corporation as he sat,
Looking little though wondrous fat;
Nor brighter was his eye, nor moister
Than a too-long-opened oyster,
Save when at noon his paunch grew mutinous
For a plate of turtle, green and glutinous.)
'Only a scraping of shoes on the mat?
Anything like the sound of a rat
Makes my heart go pit-a-pat!'

V

'Come in!' the Mayor cried, looking bigger;
And in did come the strangest figure!
His queer long coat from heel to head
Was half of yellow and half of red;
And he himself was tall and thin,
With sharp blue eyes, each like a pin,
And light loose hair, yet swarthy skin,
No tuft on cheek nor beard on chin,
But lips where smiles went out and in;
There was no guessing his kith and kin:
And nobody could enough admire
The tall man and his quaint attire.
Quoth one: 'It's as my great-grandsire
Starting up at the Trump of Doom's tone,
Had walked this way from his painted tombstone!'

VI

He advanced to the council-table:
And 'Please your honours,' he said, 'I'm able,
  By means of a secret charm, to draw
All creatures living beneath the sun,
That creep, or swim, or fly, or run,

63

After me so as you never saw!
And I chiefly use my charm
On creatures that do people harm,
The mole and toad and newt and viper;
And people call me the Pied Piper.'
(And here they noticed round his neck
  A scarf of red and yellow stripe,
To match his coat of the self-same check:
  And at the scarf's end hung a pipe:
And his fingers, they noticed, were ever straying
As if impatient to be playing
Upon this pipe, as low it dangled
Over his vesture so old-fangled.)
'Yet,' said he, 'poor piper as I am,
In Tartary I freed the Cham,
  Last June, from his huge swarm of gnats;
I eased in Asia the Nizam
  Of a monstrous brood of vampire bats:
And as for what your brain bewilders,
  If I can rid your town of rats,
Will you give me a thousand guilders?'
'One? Fifty thousand!' was the exclamation
Of the astonished Mayor and Corporation.

VII

Into the street the Piper stept,
  Smiling first a little smile,
As if he knew what magic slept
  In his quiet pipe the while;
Then, like a musical adept,
To blow the pipe his lips he wrinkled,
And green and blue his sharp eyes twinkled
Like a candle-flame where salt is sprinkled;

And ere three shrill notes the pipe uttered,
You heard as if an army muttered;
And the muttering grew to a grumbling;
And the grumbling grew to a mighty rumbling;
And out of the houses the rats came tumbling.
Great rats, small rats, lean rats, brawny rats,
Brown rats, black rats, grey rats, tawny rats,
Grave old plodders, gay young friskers,
　　Fathers, mothers, uncles, cousins,
Cocking tails and pricking whiskers,
　　Families by tens and dozens,
Brothers, sisters, husbands, wives—
Followed the Piper for their lives.
From street to street he piped advancing,
And step for step they followed dancing,
Until they came to the river Weser,
　　Wherein all plunged and perished!
—Save one who, stout as Julius Caesar,
Swam across and lived to carry
　　(As he, the manuscript he cherished)
To Rat-land home his commentary:
Which was, 'At the first shrill notes of the pipe,
I heard a sound as of scraping tripe,
And putting apples, wondrous ripe,
Into a cider-press's gripe:
And a moving away of pickle-tub-boards,
And a leaving ajar of conserve-cupboards,
And a drawing the corks of train-oil-flasks,
And a breaking the hoops of butter-casks:
And it seemed as if a voice
　　(Sweeter far than by harp or by psaltery
Is breathed) called out, "Oh rats, rejoice!
　　The world is grown to one vast drysaltery!
So munch on, crunch on, take your nuncheon,

Breakfast, supper, dinner, luncheon!"
And just as a bulky sugar-puncheon,
All ready staved, like a great sun shone
Glorious scarce an inch before me,
Just as methought it said, "Come, bore me!"
—I found the Weser rolling o'er me.'

VIII

You should have heard the Hamelin people
Ringing the bells till they rocked the steeple.
'Go,' cried the Mayor, 'and get long poles,
Poke out the nests and block up the holes!
   Consult with carpenters and builders,
And leave in our town not even a trace
Of the rats!'—when suddenly, up the face
Of the Piper perked in the market-place,
   With a, 'First, if you please, my thousand guilders!'

IX

A thousand guilders! The Mayor looked blue;
So did the Corporation too.
For council dinners made rare havoc
With Claret, Moselle, Vin-de-Grave, Hock;
And half the money would replenish
Their cellar's biggest butt with Rhenish.
To pay this sum to a wandering fellow
With a gipsy coat of red and yellow!
'Beside,' quoth the Mayor, with a knowing wink,
'Our business was done at the river's brink;
We saw with our eyes the vermin sink,
And what's dead can't come to life, I think.
So, friend, we're not the folks to shrink
From the duty of giving you something for drink,

And a matter of money to put in your poke;
But as for the guilders, what we spoke
Of them, as you very well know, was in joke.
Beside, our losses have made us thrifty.
A thousand guilders! Come, take fifty!'

X

The Piper's face fell, and he cried,
'No trifling! I can't wait, beside!
I've promised to visit by dinner-time
Bagdat, and accept the prime
Of the Head Cook's pottage, all he's rich in,
For having left, in the Caliph's kitchen,
Of a nest of scorpions no survivor:
With him I proved no bargain-driver,
With you, don't think I'll bate a stiver!
And folks who put me in a passion
May find me pipe after another fashion.'

XI

'How?' cried the Mayor, 'd'ye think I brook
Being worse treated than a Cook?
Insulted by a lazy ribald
With idle pipe and vesture piebald?
You threaten us, fellow? Do your worst,
Blow your pipe there till you burst!'

XII

Once more he stept into the street,
    And to his lips again
    Laid his long pipe of smooth straight cane;
And ere he blew three notes (such sweet
    Soft notes as yet musician's cunning

Never gave the enraptured air),
There was a rustling that seemed like a bustling
Of merry crowds justling at pitching and hustling;
Small feet were pattering, wooden shoes clattering,
Little hands clapping and little tongues chattering,
And, like fowls in a farm-yard when barley is scatter-
        ing,
    Out came the children running.
All the little boys and girls,
With rosy cheeks and flaxen curls,
And sparkling eyes and teeth like pearls,
Tripping and skipping, ran merrily after
The wonderful music with shouting and laughter.

XIII

The Mayor was dumb, and the Council stood
As if they were changed into blocks of wood,
Unable to move a step, or cry
To the children merrily skipping by,
—Could only follow with the eye
That joyous crowd at the Piper's back.
But how the Mayor was on the rack,
And the wretched Council's bosoms beat,
As the Piper turned from the High Street
To where the Weser rolled its waters
Right in the way of their sons and daughters!
However, he turned from South to West,
And to Koppelberg Hill his steps addressed,
And after him the children pressed;
Great was the joy in every breast.
'He never can cross that mighty top!
He's forced to let the piping drop,
And we shall see our children stop!'

When, lo, as they reached the mountain's side,
A wondrous portal opened wide,
As if a cavern was suddenly hollowed;
And the Piper advanced and the children followed,
And when all were in, to the very last,
The door in the mountain-side shut fast.
Did I say all? No! One was lame,
    And could not dance the whole of the way;
And in after years, if you would blame
    His sadness, he was used to say,—
'It's dull in our town since my playmates left!
I can't forget that I'm bereft
Of all the pleasant sights they see,
Which the Piper also promised me.
For he led us, he said, to a joyous land,
Joining the town, and just at hand,
Where waters gushed and fruit-trees grew,
And flowers put forth a fairer hue,
And everything was strange and new;
The sparrows were brighter than peacocks here,
And their dogs outran our fallow-deer;
And honey-bees had lost their stings,
And horses were born with eagle's wings;
And just as I became assured
My lame foot would be speedily cured,
The music stopped, and I stood still,
And found myself outside the hill,
Left alone against my will,
To go now limping as before,
And never hear of that country more!'

XIV

Alas! alas for Hamelin!
    There came into many a burgher's pate

A text which says that heaven's gate
    Opes to the rich at as easy a rate
As the needle's eye takes a camel in!
The Mayor sent east, west, north and south,
To offer the Piper, by word of mouth,
    Wherever it was man's lot to find him,
Silver and gold to his heart's content,
If he'd only return the way he went,
    And bring the children behind him.
But when they saw 'twas a lost endeavour,
And Piper and dancers were gone for ever,
They made a decree that lawyers never
    Should think their records dated duly
If, after the day of the month and year,
These words did not as well appear:
'And so long after what happened here
    On the twenty-second of July,
Thirteen hundred and seventy-six':
And the better in memory to fix
The place of the children's last retreat,
They called it the Pied Piper's Street—
Where anyone playing on pipe or tabor
Was sure for the future to lose his labour.
Nor suffered they hostelry or tavern
    To shock with mirth a street so solemn;
But opposite the place of the cavern
    They wrote the story on a column,
And on the great church window painted
The same, to make the world acquainted
How their children were stolen away,
And there it stands to this very day.
And I must not omit to say
That in Transylvania there's a tribe
Of alien people who ascribe

The outlandish ways and dress
On which their neighbours lay such stress,
To their fathers and mothers having risen
Out of some subterraneous prison
Into which they were trepanned
Long time ago in a mighty band
Out of Hamelin town in Brunswick land,
But how or why, they don't understand.

XV

So, Willy, let me and you be wipers
Of scores out with all men—especially pipers!
And, whether they pipe us free from rats or from mice,
If we've promised them aught, let us keep our promise!

ROBERT BROWNING

41 *Pibroch of Donuil Dhu*

PIBROCH of Donuil Dhu,
  Pibroch of Donuil,
Wake thy wild voice anew,
  Summon Clan Conuil.
Come away, come away,
  Hark to the summons!
Come in your war array,
  Gentles and commons.

Come from deep glen, and
  From mountain so rocky,
The war-pipe and pennon
  Are at Inverlochy.

Come every hill-plaid, and
  True heart that wears one,
Come every steel blade, and
  Strong hand that bears one.

Leave untended the herd,
  The flock without shelter;
Leave the corpse uninterr'd,
  The bride at the altar;
Leave the deer, leave the steer,
  Leave nets and barges:
Come with your fighting gear,
  Broadswords and targes.

Come as the winds come, when
  Forests are rended,
Come as the waves come, when
  Navies are stranded:
Faster come, faster come,
  Faster and faster,
Chief, vassal, page and groom,
  Tenant and master.

Fast they come, fast they come;
  See how they gather!
Wide waves the eagle plume,
  Blended with heather.
Cast your plaids, draw your blades,
  Forward, each man, set!
Pibroch of Donuil Dhu,
  Knell for the onset!

SIR W. SCOTT

Coronach

HE is gone on the mountain,
  He is lost to the forest,
Like a summer-dried fountain,
  When our need was the sorest.
The font reappearing
  From the raindrops shall borrow,
But to us comes no cheering,
  To Duncan no morrow!

The hand of the reaper
  Takes the ears that are hoary,
But the voice of the weeper
  Wails manhood in glory.
The autumn winds rushing
  Waft the leaves that are serest,
But our flower was in flushing
  When blighting was nearest.

Fleet foot on the correi,
  Sage counsel in cumber,
Red hand in the foray,
  How sound is thy slumber!
Like the dew on the mountain,
  Like the foam on the river,
Like the bubble on the fountain,
  Thou art gone, and for ever!

                              SIR W. SCOTT

Will Ye No Come Back Again?

BONNIE Charlie's now awa',
  Safely ower the friendly main;
Mony a heart will break in twa
  Should he ne'er come back again?

  Will ye no come back again?
  Will ye no come back again?
  Better lo'ed ye canna be—
  Will ye no come back again?

Ye trusted in your Hieland men,
  They trusted you, dear Charlie!
They kent your hiding in the glen,
  Death or exile braving.
    Will ye no, &c.

English bribes were a' in vain,
  Tho' puir, and puirer, we maun be;
Siller canna buy the heart
  That beats aye for thine and thee.
    Will ye no, &c.

We watch'd thee in the gloamin' hour,
  We watch'd thee in the mornin' grey;
Though thirty thousand pound they gi'e,
  Oh, there is none that wad betray!
    Will ye no, &c.

Sweet's the laverock's note, and lang,
  Lilting wildly up the glen;
But aye to me he sings ae sang,
  Will ye no come back again?
    Will ye no, &c.

LADY C. NAIRNE

MARCHING ALONG

KENTISH Sir Byng stood for his King,
Bidding the crop-headed Parliament swing:
And, pressing a troop unable to stoop
And see the rogues flourish and honest folk droop,
Marched them along, fifty-score strong,
Great-hearted gentlemen, singing this song.

God for King Charles! Pym and such carles
To the Devil that prompts 'em their treasonous parles!
Cavaliers, up! Lips from the cup,
Hands from the pasty, nor bite take nor sup
Till you're—
    CHORUS.—Marching along, fifty-score strong,
           Great-hearted gentlemen, singing this song.

Hampden to hell, and his obsequies' knell
Serve Hazelrig, Fiennes, and young Harry as well!
England, good cheer! Rupert is near!
Kentish and loyalists, keep we not here
    CHORUS.—Marching along, fifty-score strong,
           Great-hearted gentlemen, singing this song?

Then, God for King Charles! Pym and his snarls
To the Devil that pricks on such pestilent carles!
Hold by the right, you double your might;
So, onward to Nottingham, fresh for the fight,
    CHORUS.—March we along, fifty-score strong,
           Great-hearted gentlemen, singing this song!

KING Charles, and who'll do him right now?
King Charles, and who's ripe for fight now?
Give a rouse: here's, in hell's despite now,
King Charles!

Who gave me the goods that went since?
Who raised me the house that sank once?
Who helped me to gold I spent since?
Who found me in wine you drank once?
  CHORUS.—King Charles, and who'll do him right now?
            King Charles, and who's ripe for fight now?
            Give a rouse: here's, in hell's despite now,
            King Charles!

To whom used my boy George quaff else,
By the old fool's side that begot him?
For whom did he cheer and laugh else,
While Noll's damned troopers shot him?
  CHORUS.—King Charles, and who'll do him right now?
            King Charles, and who's ripe for fight now?
            Give a rouse: here's, in hell's despite now,
            King Charles!

BOOT AND SADDLE

BOOT, saddle, to horse, and away!
Rescue my castle before the hot day
Brightens to blue from its silvery grey,
  CHORUS.—Boot, saddle, to horse, and away!

Ride past the suburbs, asleep as you'd say;
Many's the friend there, will listen and pray
'God's luck to gallants that strike up the lay—
    CHORUS.—'Boot, saddle, to horse, and away!'

Forty miles off, like a roebuck at bay,
Flouts Castle Brancepeth the Roundheads' array:
Who laughs, 'Good fellows ere this, by my fay,
    CHORUS.—'Boot, saddle, to horse, and away!'

Who? My wife Gertrude; that, honest and gay,
Laughs when you talk of surrendering, 'Nay!
'I've better counsellors; what counsel they?
    CHORUS.—'Boot, saddle, to horse, and away!'
                  ROBERT BROWNING

45   *The Charge of the Light Brigade*

HALF a league, half a league,
  Half a league onward,
All in the valley of Death
  Rode the six hundred.
'Forward, the Light Brigade!
Charge for the guns!' he said:
Into the valley of Death
  Rode the six hundred.

'Forward, the Light Brigade!'
Was there a man dismay'd?
Not tho' the soldier knew
  Someone had blundered.
Theirs not to make reply,

Theirs not to reason why,
Theirs but to do and die:
Into the valley of Death
  Rode the six hundred.

Cannon to right of them,
Cannon to left of them,
Cannon in front of them
  Volley'd and thunder'd;
Storm'd at with shot and shell,
Boldly they rode and well,
Into the jaws of Death,
Into the mouth of Hell
  Rode the six hundred.

Flash'd all their sabres bare,
Flash'd as they turn'd in air
Sabring the gunners there,
Charging an army, while
  All the world wonder'd:
Plung'd in the battery-smoke
Right thro' the line they broke;
Cossack and Russian
Reel'd from the sabre-stroke
  Shatter'd and sunder'd.
Then they rode back, but not,
  Not the six hundred.

Cannon to right of them,
Cannon to left of them,
Cannon behind them
  Volley'd and thunder'd;
Storm'd at with shot and shell,
While horse and hero fell,

They that had fought so well
Came thro' the jaws of Death,
Back from the mouth of Hell,
All that was left of them,
  Left of six hundred.

When can their glory fade?
O the wild charge they made!
  All the world wonder'd.
Honour the charge they made!
Honour the Light Brigade,
  Noble six hundred!

LORD TENNYSON

46 *Agincourt*

FAIR stood the wind for France
When we our sails advance,
Nor now to prove our chance
    Longer will tarry;
But putting to the main,
At Caux, the mouth of Seine,
With all his martial train
    Landed King Harry.

And taking many a fort,
Furnished in warlike sort,
Marched towards Agincourt
    In happy hour;
Skirmishing day by day
With those that stopped his way,
Where the French general lay
    With all his power.

Which, in his height of pride,
King Henry to deride,
His ransom to provide
    Unto him sending;
Which he neglects the while,
As from a nation vile,
Yet with an angry smile
    Their fall portending.

And turning to his men,
Quoth our brave Henry then,
'Though they to one be ten,
    Be not amazèd:
Yet, have we well begun;
Battles so bravely won
Have ever to the sun
    By fame been raisèd.

'And for myself,' (quoth he):
'This my full rest shall be:
England ne'er mourn for me
    Nor more esteem me:
Victor I will remain
Or on this earth lie slain;
Never shall she sustain
    Loss to redeem me.

'Poitiers and Cressy tell,
When most their pride did swell,
Under our swords they fell:
    No less our skill is
Than when our grandsire great,
Claiming the regal seat,
By many a warlike feat
    Lopp'd the French lilies.'

The Duke of York so dread
The eager vaward led;
With the main Henry sped
    Among his henchmen.
Excester had the rear,
A braver man not there;
O Lord, how hot they were
    On the false Frenchmen!

They now to fight are gone,
Armour on armour shone,
Drum now to drum did groan,
    To hear was wonder;
That with the cries they make
The very earth did shake:
Trumpet to trumpet spake,
    Thunder to thunder.

Well it thine age became,
O noble Erpingham,
Which didst the signal aim
    To our hid forces!
When from a meadow by,
Like a storm suddenly
The English archery
    Struck the French horses.

With Spanish yew so strong,
Arrows a cloth-yard long
That like to serpents stung,
    Piercing the weather;
None from his fellow starts,
But playing manly parts,
And like true English hearts
    Stuck close together.

81

When down their bows they threw,
And forth their bilbos drew,
And on the French they flew,
    Not one was tardy;
Arms were from shoulders sent,
Scalps to the teeth were rent,
Down the French peasants went—
    Our men were hardy!

This while our noble king,
His broadsword brandishing,
Down the French host did ding
    As to o'erwhelm it;
And many a deep wound lent,
His arms with blood besprent,
And many a cruel dent
    Bruisèd his helmet.

Gloster, that duke so good,
Next of the royal blood,
For famous England stood
    With his brave brother;
Clarence, in steel so bright,
Though but a maiden knight,
Yet in that furious fight
    Scarce such another.

Warwick in blood did wade,
Oxford the foe invade,
And cruel slaughter made
    Still as they ran up;
Suffolk his axe did ply,
Beaumont and Willoughby
Bare them right doughtily,
    Ferrers and Fanhope.

Upon Saint Crispin's Day
Fought was this noble fray,
Which fame did not delay
   To England to carry.
O when shall English men
With such acts fill a pen,
Or England breed again
   Such a King Harry?

       M. DRAYTON

47 *Horatius*

LARS PORSENA of Clusium
  By the nine Gods he swore
That the great house of Tarquin
  Should suffer wrong no more.
By the nine Gods he swore it,
  And named a trysting day,
And bade his messengers ride forth,
East and west and south and north,
  To summon his array.

East and west and south and north
  The messengers ride fast,
And tower and town and cottage
  Have heard the trumpet's blast.
Shame on the false Etruscan
  Who lingers in his home,
When Porsena of Clusium
  Is on the march for Rome!

The horsemen and the footmen
　　Are pouring in amain
From many a stately market-place,
　　From many a fruitful plain,
From many a lonely hamlet,
　　Which, hid by beech and pine,
Like an eagle's nest hangs on the crest
　　Of purple Apennine.

Tall are the oaks whose acorns
　　Drop in dark Auser's rill;
Fat are the stags that champ the boughs
　　Of the Ciminian hill;
Beyond all streams Clitumnus
　　Is to the herdsman dear;
Best of all pools the fowler loves
　　The Great Volsinian mere.

But now no stroke of woodman
　　Is heard by Auser's rill;
No hunter tracks the stag's green path
　　Up the Ciminian hill;
Unwatched along Clitumnus
　　Grazes the milk-white steer;
Unharmed the water-fowl may dip
　　In the Volsinian mere.

The harvests of Arretium,
　　This year, old men shall reap,
This year, young boys in Umbro
　　Shall plunge the struggling sheep;
And in the vats of Luna,
　　This year, the must shall foam
Round the white feet of laughing girls
　　Whose sires have marched to Rome.

And now hath every city
  Sent up her tale of men;
The foot are fourscore thousand,
  The horse are thousands ten:
Before the gates of Sutrium
  Is met the great array.
A proud man was Lars Porsena
  Upon the trysting day.

But by the yellow Tiber
  Was tumult and affright:
From all the spacious champaign
  To Rome men took their flight.
A mile around the city,
  The throng stopped up the ways;
A fearful sight it was to see
  Through two long nights and days.

Now, from the rock Tarpeian,
  Could the wan burghers spy
The line of blazing villages
  Red in the midnight sky.
The Fathers of the City,
  They sat all night and day,
For every hour some horseman came
  With tidings of dismay.

To eastward and to westward
  Have spread the Tuscan bands;
Nor house, nor fence, nor dovecote
  In Crustumerium stands.
Verbenna down to Ostia
  Hath wasted all the plain;
Astur hath stormed Janiculum,
  And the stout guards are slain.

I-wis, in all the Senate,
  There was no heart so bold,
But sore it ached and fast it beat,
  When that ill news was told.
Forthwith uprose the Consul,
  Uprose the Fathers all;
In haste they girded up their gowns,
  And hied them to the wall.

They held a council standing
  Before the River-Gate;
Short time was there, ye well may guess,
  For musing or debate.
Out spake the Consul roundly:
  'The bridge must straight go down;
For, since Janiculum is lost,
  Nought else can save the town.'

Just then a scout came flying,
  All wild with haste and fear:
'To arms! to arms! Sir Consul:
  Lars Porsena is here.'
On the low hills to westward
  The Consul fixed his eye,
And saw the swarthy storm of dust
  Rise fast along the sky.

And nearer fast and nearer
  Doth the red whirlwind come;
And louder still and still more loud,
From underneath that rolling cloud,
Is heard the trumpet's war-note proud,
  The trampling and the hum.

And plainly and more plainly
  Now through the gloom appears,
Far to the left and far to right,
In broken gleams of dark-blue light,
The long array of helmets bright,
  The long array of spears.

Fast by the royal standard,
  O'erlooking all the war,
Lars Porsena of Clusium
  Sat in his ivory car.
By the right wheel rode Mamilius,
  Prince of the Latian name;
And by the left false Sextus,
  That wrought the deed of shame.

But when the face of Sextus
  Was seen among the foes,
A yell that rent the firmament
  From all the town arose.
On the house-tops was no woman
  But spat towards him and hissed;
No child but screamed out curses,
  And shook its little fist.

But the Consul's brow was sad,
  And the Consul's speech was low,
And darkly looked he at the wall,
  And darkly at the foe.
'Their van will be upon us
  Before the bridge goes down;
And if they once may win the bridge
  What hope to save the town?'

Then out spake brave Horatius,
    The Captain of the Gate:
'To every man upon this earth
    Death cometh soon or late.
And how can man die better
    Than facing fearful odds,
For the ashes of his fathers,
    And the temples of his Gods,

'And for the tender mother
    Who dandled him to rest,
And for the wife who nurses
    His baby at her breast,
And for the holy maidens
    Who feed the eternal flame,
To save them from false Sextus,
    That wrought the deed of shame?

'Hew down the bridge, Sir Consul,
    With all the speed ye may;
I, with two more to help me,
    Will hold the foe in play.
In yon strait path a thousand
    May well be stopped by three.
Now who will stand on either hand,
    And keep the bridge with me?'

Then out spake Spurius Lartius;
    A Ramnian proud was he:
'Lo, I will stand at thy right hand,
    And keep the bridge with thee.'
And out spake strong Herminius;
    Of Titian blood was he:
'I will abide on thy left side,
    And keep the bridge with thee.'

'Horatius,' quoth the Consul,
  'As thou sayest, so let it be.'
And straight against that great array
  Forth went the dauntless Three.
For Romans in Rome's quarrel
  Spared neither land nòr gold,
Nor son nor wife, nor limb nor life,
  In the brave days of old.

Then none was for a party;
  Then all were for the State;
Then the great man helped the poor,
  And the poor man loved the great:
Then lands were fairly portioned;
  Then spoils were fairly sold:
The Romans were like brothers
  In the brave days of old.

Now while the Three were tightening
  Their harness on their backs,
The Consul was the foremost man
  To take in hand an axe:
And Fathers mixed with Commons
  Seized hatchet, bar, and crow,
And smote upon the planks above,
  And loosed the props below.

Meanwhile the Tuscan army,
  Right glorious to behold,
Came flashing back the noonday light,
Rank behind rank, like surges bright
  Of a broad sea of gold.
Four hundred trumpets sounded
  A peal of warlike glee,

As that great host, with measured tread,
And spears advanced, and ensigns spread,
Rolled slowly towards the bridge's head,
  Where stood the dauntless Three.

The Three stood calm and silent,
  And looked upon the foes,
And a great shout of laughter
  From all the vanguard rose:
And forth three chiefs came spurring
  Before that deep array;
To earth they sprang, their swords they drew,
And lifted high their shields, and flew
  To win the narrow way:

Aunus from green Tifernum,
  Lord of the Hill of Vines;
And Seius, whose eight hundred slaves
  Sicken in Ilva's mines;
And Picus, long to Clusium
  Vassal in peace and war,
Who led to fight his Umbrian powers
From that grey crag where, girt with towers,
The fortress of Nequinum lowers
  O'er the pale waves of Nar.

Stout Lartius hurled down Aunus
  Into the stream beneath:
Herminius struck at Seius,
  And clove him to the teeth:
At Picus brave Horatius
  Darted one fiery thrust;
And the proud Umbrian's gilded arms
  Clashed in the bloody dust.

Then Ocnus of Falerii
   Rushed on the Roman three;
And Lausulus of Urgo,
   The rover of the sea;
And Aruns of Volsinium
   Who slew the great wild boar,
The great wild boar that had his den
Amidst the reeds of Cosa's fen,
And wasted fields, and slaughtered men,
   Along Albinia's shore.

Herminius smote down Aruns:
   Lartius laid Ocnus low:
Right to the heart of Lausulus
   Horatius sent a blow.
'Lie there,' he cried, 'fell pirate!
   No more, aghast and pale,
From Ostia's wall the crowd shall mark
The track of thy destroying bark.
No more Campania's hinds shall fly
To woods and caverns when they spy
   Thy thrice-accursèd sail.'

But now no sound of laughter
   Was heard among the foes,
A wild and wrathful clamour
   From all the vanguard rose.
Six spears' lengths from the entrance
   Halted that deep array,
And for a space no man came forth
   To win the narrow way.

But hark! the cry is 'Astur!'
  And lo! the ranks divide;
And the great Lord of Luna
  Comes with his stately stride.
Upon his ample shoulders
  Clangs loud the fourfold shield,
And in his hand he shakes the brand
  Which none but he can wield.

He smiled on those bold Romans
  A smile serene and high;
He eyed the flinching Tuscans,
  And scorn was in his eye.
Quoth he, 'The she-wolf's litter
  Stands savagely at bay:
But will ye dare to follow,
  If Astur clears the way?'

Then, whirling up his broadsword
  With both hands to the height,
He rushed against Horatius,
  And smote with all his might.
With shield and blade Horatius
  Right deftly turned the blow.
The blow, though turned, came yet too nigh;
It missed his helm, but gashed his thigh:
The Tuscans raised a joyful cry
  To see the red blood flow.

He reeled, and on Herminius
  He leaned one breathing-space;
Then, like a wild cat mad with wounds,
  Sprang right at Astur's face.

Through teeth, and skull, and helmet,
  So fierce a thrust he sped,
The good sword stood a hand-breadth out
  Behind the Tuscan's head.

And the great Lord of Luna
  Fell at that deadly stroke
As falls on Mount Alvernus
  A thunder-smitten oak;
Far o'er the crashing forest
  The giant arms lie spread,
And the pale augurs, muttering low,
  Gaze on the blasted head.

On Astur's throat Horatius
  Right firmly pressed his heel,
And thrice and four times tugged amain,
  Ere he wrenched out the steel.
'And see,' he cried, 'the welcome,
  Fair guests, that waits you here!
What noble Lucumo comes next
  To taste our Roman cheer?'

But at his haughty challenge
  A sullen murmur ran,
Mingled of wrath, and shame, and dread,
  Along that glittering van.
There lacked not men of prowess,
  Nor men of lordly race;
For all Etruria's noblest
  Were round the fatal place.

But all Etruria's noblest
  Felt their hearts sink to see
On the earth the bloody corpses,
  In the path the dauntless Three;
And, from the ghastly entrance,
  Where those bold Romans stood,
All shrank, like boys who, unaware,
Ranging the woods to start a hare,
Come to the mouth of the dark lair
Where, growling low, a fierce old bear
  Lies amidst bones and blood.

Was none who would be foremost
  To lead such dire attack:
But those behind cried 'Forward!'
  And those before cried 'Back!'
And backward now and forward
  Wavers the deep array;
And on the tossing sea of steel,
To and fro the standards reel;
And the victorious trumpet-peal
  Dies fitfully away.

But meanwhile axe and lever
  Have manfully been plied;
And now the bridge hangs tottering
  Above the boiling tide.
'Come back, come back, Horatius!'
  Loud cried the Fathers all.
'Back, Lartius! back, Herminius!
  Back, ere the ruin fall!'

Back darted Spurius Lartius;
    Herminius darted back:
And, as they passed, beneath their feet
    They felt the timbers crack.
But when they turned their faces,
    And on the farther shore
Saw brave Horatius stand alone,
    They would have crossed once more.

But with a crash like thunder
    Fell every loosened beam,
And, like a dam, the mighty wreck
    Lay right athwart the stream.
And a long shout of triumph
    Rose from the walls of Rome,
As to the highest turret-tops
    Was splashed the yellow foam.

And, like a horse unbroken
    When first he feels the rein,
The furious river struggled hard,
    And tossed his tawny-mane,
And burst the curb, and bounded,
    Rejoicing to be free,
And whirling down, in fierce career,
Battlement, and plank, and pier
    Rushed headlong to the sea.

Alone stood brave Horatius,
    But constant still in mind;
Thrice thirty thousand foes before,
    And the broad flood behind.

'Down with him!' cried false Sextus,
  With a smile on his pale face.
'Now yield thee,' cried Lars Porsena,
  'Now yield thee to our grace.'

Round turned he, as not deigning
  Those craven ranks to see;
Nought spake he to Lars Porsena,
  To Sextus nought spake he:
But he saw on Palatinus
  The white porch of his home;
And he spake to the noble river
  That rolls by the towers of Rome.

'Oh, Tiber! father Tiber!
  To whom the Romans pray,
A Roman's life, a Roman's arms,
  Take thou in charge this day!'
So he spake, and speaking sheathed
  The good sword by his side,
And with his harness on his back
  Plunged headlong in the tide.

No sound of joy or sorrow
  Was heard from either bank;
But friends and foes in dumb surprise,
With parted lips and straining eyes,
  Stood gazing where he sank;
And when above the surges
  They saw his crest appear,
All Rome sent forth a rapturous cry,
And even the ranks of Tuscany
  Could scarce forbear to cheer.

But fiercely ran the current,
  Swollen high by months of rain:
And fast his blood was flowing;
  And he was sore in pain,
And heavy with his armour,
  And spent with changing blows:
And oft they thought him sinking,
  But still again he rose.

Never, I ween, did swimmer,
  In such an evil case,
Struggle through such a raging flood
  Safe to the landing-place;
But his limbs were borne up bravely
  By the brave heart within,
And our good father Tiber
  Bare bravely up his chin.

'Curse on him!' quoth false Sextus;
  'Will not the villain drown?
But for this stay, ere close of day
  We should have sacked the town!'
'Heaven help him!' quoth Lars Porsena,
  'And bring him safe to shore;
For such a gallant feat of arms
  Was never seen before.'

And now he feels the bottom;
  Now on dry earth he stands;
Now round him throng the Fathers
  To press his gory hands;
And now, with shouts and clapping,
  And noise of weeping loud,
He enters through the River-Gate,
  Borne by the joyous crowd.

They gave him of the corn-land,
  That was of public right,
As much as two strong oxen
  Could plough from morn till night;
And they made a molten image,
  And set it up on high,
And there it stands unto this day
  To witness if I lie.

It stands in the Comitium,
  Plain for all folk to see;
Horatius in his harness,
  Halting upon one knee;
And underneath is written,
  In letters all of gold,
How valiantly he kept the bridge
  In the brave days of old.

And still his name sounds stirring
  Unto the men of Rome,
As the trumpet-blast that cries to them
  To charge the Volscian home.
And wives still pray to Juno
  For boys with hearts as bold
As his who kept the bridge so well
  In the brave days of old.

And in the nights of winter,
  When the cold north winds blow,
And the long howling of the wolves
  Is heard amidst the snow;
When round the lonely cottage
  Roars loud the tempest's din,
And the good logs of Algidus
  Roar louder yet within;

When the oldest cask is opened,
    And the largest lamp is lit;
When the chestnuts glow in the embers,
    And the kid turns on the spit;
When young and old in circle
    Around the firebrands close;
When the girls are weaving baskets,
    And the lads are shaping bows;

When the goodman mends his armour,
    And trims his helmet's plume;
When the goodwife's shuttle merrily
    Goes flashing through the loom;
With weeping and with laughter
    Still is the story told,
How well Horatius kept the bridge
    In the brave days of old.

                        LORD MACAULAY

48   *Winter*

WHEN icicles hang by the wall,
    And Dick the shepherd blows his nail,
And Tom bears logs into the hall,
    And milk comes frozen home in pail,
When blood is nipt, and ways be foul,
Then nightly sings the staring owl
                    Tuwhoo!
Tuwhit! tuwhoo! A merry note,
While greasy Joan doth keel the pot.

When all around the wind doth blow,
 And coughing drowns the parson's saw,
And birds sit brooding in the snow,
 And Marian's nose looks red and raw:
When roasted crabs hiss in the bowl—
Then nightly sings the staring owl
                    Tuwhoo!
Tuwhit! tuwhoo! A merry note,
While greasy Joan doth keel the pot.
                              W. SHAKESPEARE

49 *Stopping by Woods on a Snowy Evening*

WHOSE woods these are I think I know.
His house is in the village though;
He will not see me stopping here
To watch his woods fill up with snow.

My little horse must think it queer
To stop without a farmhouse near
Between the woods and frozen lake
The darkest evening of the year.

He gives his harness bells a shake
To ask if there is some mistake.
The only other sound's the sweep
Of easy wind and downy flake.

The woods are lovely, dark and deep,
But I have promises to keep,
And miles to go before I sleep,
And miles to go before I sleep.
                              ROBERT FROST

BLOW, blow, thou winter wind,
Thou art not so unkind
    As man's ingratitude;
Thy tooth is not so keen,
Because thou art not seen,
    Although thy breath be rude.
Heigh-ho! sing, heigh-ho! unto the green holly:
Most friendship is feigning, most loving mere folly:
    Then heigh-ho the holly!
    This life is most jolly.

Freeze, freeze, thou bitter sky,
That dost not bite so nigh
    As benefits forgot:
Though thou the waters warp,
Thy sting is not so sharp
    As friend remember'd not.
Heigh-ho! sing, heigh-ho! unto the green holly:
Most friendship is feigning, most loving mere folly:
    Then heigh-ho the holly!
    This life is most jolly.

                                    W. SHAKESPEARE

51   *April*

I MUST go back to a vest again, to a winter vest with sleeves,
And all I ask is an honest shop where the shop-men are not
        thieves;
And a fair price, and a free choice, and a full stretch for
        dining,
And a smooth touch on the bare chest, and a smooth inner
        lining.

I must go back to a vest again, for that which most I dread
Is a bad cold, a head cold, and a day, or more, in bed;
And all I ask is a friend's advice, and a short time for think-
    ing,
A soft wool, and a man's size, and a good bit for shrinking.

I must go back to a vest again, for the April winds are bleak,
And the spring's way is a cold way, and my circulation weak;
And all I ask, when the cash is paid and we leave the shop
    together,
Is a warm fire and an armchair, or a change in the weather.

G. F. BRADBY

52   *The Scarecrow*

ALL winter through I bow my head
        Beneath the driving rain;
The North Wind powders me with snow
        And blows me black again;
At midnight in a maze of stars
        I flame with glittering rime,
And stand, above the stubble, stiff
        As mail at morning-prime.
But when that child, called Spring, and all
        His host of children, come,
Scattering their buds and dew upon
        These acres of my home,
Some rapture in my rags awakes;
        I lift void eyes and scan
The skies for crows, those ravening foes,
        Of my strange master, Man.

I watch him striding lank behind
  His clashing team, and know
Soon will the wheat swish body high
  Where once lay sterile snow;
Soon shall I gaze across a sea
  Of sun-begotten grain,
Which my unflinching watch hath sealed
  For harvest once again.
                    WALTER DE LA MARE

53   *The Cock is Crowing*

THE Cock is crowing,
The stream is flowing,
The small birds twitter,
The lake doth glitter,
The green field sleeps in the sun:
  The oldest and youngest
  Are at work with the strongest;
  The cattle are grazing,
  Their heads never raising;
There are forty feeding like one!

  Like an army defeated
  The snow hath retreated,
  And now doth fare ill
  On the top of the bare hill;
The Ploughboy is whooping—anon—anon:
  There's joy in the mountains;
  There's life in the fountains;
  Small clouds are sailing,
  Blue sky prevailing;
The rain is over and gone!
                    W. WORDSWORTH

Pippa's Song

THE year's at the spring
And day's at the morn;
Morning's at seven;
The hill-side's dew-pearled;
The lark's on the wing;
The snail's on the thorn:
God's in his heaven—
All's right with the world!

ROBERT BROWNING

55

Cuckoo

SUMER is icumen in,
    Lhude sing cuccu!
Groweth sed, and bloweth med,
    And springeth the wude nu—
        Sing cuccu!

Awe bleteth after lomb,
    Lhouth after calve cu;
Bulluc sterteth, bucke verteth,
    Murie sing cuccu!

Cuccu, cuccu, well singes thu, cuccu:
    Ne swike thu naver nu;
Sing cuccu, nu, sing cuccu,
    Sing cuccu, sing cuccu, nu!

OLD SONG

awe, ewe.   lhouth, loweth.   cu, cow.   sterteth, leaps.
                    swike, cease.

THIS is the weather the cuckoo likes,
 And so do I;
When showers betumble the chestnut spikes,
 And nestlings fly;
And the little brown nightingale bills his best,
And they sit outside at 'The Travellers' Rest,'
And maids come forth sprig-muslin drest,
And citizens dream of the south and west,
 And so do I.

This is the weather the shepherd shuns,
 And so do I;
When beeches drip in browns and duns,
 And thresh, and ply;
And hill-hid tides throb, throe on throe,
And meadow rivulets overflow,
And drops on gate-bars hang in a row,
And rooks in families homeward go,
 And so do I.

THOMAS HARDY

57 *It was a Lover and his Lass*

IT was a lover and his lass,
 With a hey, and a ho, and a hey nonino,
That o'er the green corn-field did pass,
 In the spring time, the only pretty ring time,
When birds do sing, hey ding a ding, ding;
Sweet lovers love the spring.

Between the acres of the rye,
　　With a hey, and a ho, and a hey nonino,
These pretty country folks would lie,
　　In the spring time, the only pretty ring time,
When birds do sing, hey ding a ding, ding;
Sweet lovers love the spring.

This carol they began that hour,
　　With a hey, and a ho, and a hey nonino,
How that life was but a flower
　　In the spring time, the only pretty ring time,
When birds do sing, hey ding a ding, ding;
Sweet lovers love the spring.

And therefore take the present time
　　With a hey, and a ho, and a hey nonino;
For love is crowned with the prime
　　In the spring time, the only pretty ring time,
When birds do sing, hey ding a ding, ding;
Sweet lovers love the spring.

W. SHAKESPEARE

58 *The Flower-fed Buffaloes*

THE flower-fed buffaloes of the spring
In the days of long ago,
Ranged where the locomotives sing
And the prairie flowers lie low:—
The tossing, blooming, perfumed grass
Is swept away by the wheat,
Wheels and wheels and wheels spin by
In the spring that still is sweet.

But the flower-fed buffaloes of the spring
Left us, long ago.
They gore no more, they bellow no more,
They trundle around the hills no more—
With the Blackfeet, lying low,
With the Pawnees, lying low,
  Lying low.

VACHEL LINDSAY

59   *Hiawatha's Childhood*

By the shores of Gitche Gumee,
By the shining Big-Sea-Water,
Stood the wigwam of Nokomis,
Daughter of the Moon Nokomis.
Dark behind it rose the forest,
Rose the black and gloomy pine-trees,
Rose the firs with cones upon them;
Bright before it beat the water,
Beat the shining Big-Sea-Water.
  Thus the wrinkled, old Nokomis
Nursed the little Hiawatha,
Rocked him in his linden cradle,
Bedded soft in moss and rushes,
Safely bound with reindeer sinews;
Stilled his fretful wail by saying,
'Hush! the naked bear will get thee!'
Lulled him into slumber, singing,
'Ewa-yea! my little owlet!
Who is this, that lights the wigwam?
With his great eyes lights the wigwam?
Ewa-yea! my little owlet!'

Many things Nokomis taught him
Of the stars that shine in heaven;
Showed him Ishkoodah, the comet,
Ishkoodah, with fiery tresses;
Showed the Death-Dance of the spirits,
Warriors with their plumes and war-clubs,
Flaring far away to northward
In the frosty nights of Winter;
Showed the broad, white road in heaven,
Pathway of the ghosts, the shadows,
Running straight across the heavens,
Crowded with the ghosts, the shadows.

At the door on Summer evenings
Sat the little Hiawatha;
Heard the whispering of the pine-trees,
Heard the lapping of the water,
Sounds of music, words of wonder;
'Minne-wawa!' said the pine-trees,
'Mudway-aushka!' said the water.

Saw the fire-fly, Wah-wah-taysee,
Flitting through the dusk of evening,
With the twinkle of its candle
Lighting up the brakes and bushes,
And he sang the song of children,
Sang the song Nokomis taught him:
'Wah-wah-taysee, little fire-fly,
Little, flitting, white-fire insect,
Little, dancing, white-fire creature,
Light me with your little candle,
Ere upon my bed I lay me,
Ere in sleep I close my eyelids!'

Saw the moon rise from the water,
Rippling, rounding, from the water,
Saw the flecks and shadows on it,

Whispered, 'What is that, Nokomis?'
And the good Nokomis answered:
'Once a warrior, very angry,
Seized his grandmother, and threw her
Up into the sky at midnight;
Right against the moon he threw her;
'Tis her body that you see there.'

Saw the rainbow in the heaven,
In the eastern sky the rainbow,
Whispered, 'What is that, Nokomis?'
And the good Nokomis answered:
''Tis the heaven of flowers you see there,
All the wild-flowers of the forest,
All the lilies of the prairie,
When on earth they fade and perish,
Blossom in that heaven above us.'

When he heard the owls at midnight,
Hooting, laughing in the forest,
'What is that?' he cried in terror,
'What is that?' he said, 'Nokomis?'
And the good Nokomis answered:
'That is but the owl and owlet,
Talking in their native language,
Talking, scolding at each other.'

Then the little Hiawatha
Learned of every bird its language,
Learned their names and all their secrets,
How they built their nests in Summer,
Where they hid themselves in Winter,
Talked with them whene'er he met them,
Called them, 'Hiawatha's Chickens.'

Of all the beasts he learned the language,
Learned their names and all their secrets,
How the beavers built their lodges,

Where the squirrels hid their acorns,
How the reindeer ran so swiftly,
Why the rabbit was so timid,
Talked with them whene'er he met them,
Called them, 'Hiawatha's Brothers.'
　　Then Iagoo, the great boaster,
He the marvellous story-teller,
He the traveller and the talker,
He the friend of old Nokomis,
Made a bow for Hiawatha;
From a branch of ash he made it,
From an oak-bough made the arrows,
Tipped with flint, and winged with feathers,
And the cord he made of deer-skin.
　　Then he said to Hiawatha—
'Go, my son, into the forest,
Where the red deer herd together,
Kill for us a famous roebuck,
Kill for us a deer with antlers!'
　　Forth into the forest straightway
All alone walked Hiawatha
Proudly, with his bow and arrows;
And the birds sang round him, o'er him,
'Do not shoot us, Hiawatha!'
Sang the robin, the Opechee,
Sang the blue-bird, the Owaissa,
'Do not shoot us, Hiawatha!'
　　Up the oak-tree, close beside him,
Sprang the squirrel, Adjidaumo,
In and out among the branches,
Coughed and chattered from the oak-tree,
Laughed, and said between his laughing,
'Do not shoot me, Hiawatha!'
　　And the rabbit from his pathway

Leaped aside, and at a distance
Sat erect upon his haunches,
Half in fear and half in frolic,
Saying to the little hunter,
'Do not shoot me, Hiawatha!'

But he heeded not, nor heard them,
For his thoughts were with the red-deer;
On their tracks his eyes were fastened,
Leading downward to the river,
To the ford across the river,
And as one in slumber walked he.

Hidden in the alder-bushes,
There he waited till the deer came,
Till he saw two antlers lifted,
Saw two eyes look from the thicket,
Saw two nostrils point to windward,
And a deer came down the pathway,
Flecked with leafy light and shadow,
And his heart within him fluttered,
Trembled like the leaves above him,
Like the birch-leaf palpitated,
As the deer came down the pathway.

Then, upon one knee uprising,
Hiawatha aimed an arrow;
Scarce a twig moved with his motion
Scarce a leaf was stirred or rustled,
But the wary roebuck started,
Stamped with all his hoofs together,
Listened with one foot uplifted,
Leaped as if to meet the arrow;
Ah! the singing, fatal arrow,
Like a wasp it buzzed and stung him.

Dead he lay there in the forest,
By the ford across the river;

Beat his timid heart no longer,
But the heart of Hiawatha
Throbbed and shouted and exulted,
As he bore the red deer homeward,
And Iagoo and Nokomis
Hailed his coming with applauses.

From the red deer's hide Nokomis
Made a cloak for Hiawatha,
From the red deer's flesh Nokomis
Made a banquet in his honour.
All the village came and feasted,
All the guests praised Hiawatha,
Called him Strong-Heart, Soan-getaha!
Called him Loon-Heart, Mahn-go-taysee!

H. W. LONGFELLOW

60 *Hiawatha's Mittens*

WHEN he killed the Mudjekeewis,
Of the skin he made him mittens,
Made them with the fur side inside,
Made them with the skin side outside,
He, to get the warm side inside,
Put the inside skin side outside;
He, to get the cold side outside,
Put the warm side fur side inside.
That's why he put fur side inside,
Why he put the skin side outside,
Why he turned them inside outside.

ANON

ERE Mor the Peacock flutters, ere the Monkey People cry,
    Ere Chil the Kite swoops down a furlong sheer,
Through the Jungle very softly flits a Shadow and a sigh—
    He is Fear, O Little Hunter, he is Fear!
Very softly down the glade runs a waiting, watching shade,
    And the whisper spreads and widens far and near.
And the sweat is on thy brow, for he passes even now—
    He is Fear, O Little Hunter, he is Fear!

Ere the Moon has climbed the mountain, ere the rocks are
        ribbed with light,
    When the downward-dipping trails are dank and drear,
Comes a breathing hard behind thee—*snuffle-snuffle* through
        the night—
    It is Fear, O Little Hunter, it is Fear!
On thy knees and draw the bow; bid the shrilling arrow go;
    In the empty, mocking thicket plunge the spear!
But thy hands are loosed and weak, and the blood has left thy
        cheek—
    It is Fear, O Little Hunter, it is Fear!

When the heat-cloud sucks the tempest, when the slivered
        pine trees fall,
    When the blinding, blaring rain-squalls lash and veer,
Through the war-gongs of the thunder rings a voice more
        loud than all—
    It is Fear, O Little Hunter, it is Fear!
Now the spates are banked and deep; now the footless
        boulders leap—
    Now the lightning shows each littlest leaf-rib clear—
But thy throat is shut and dried, and thy heart against thy side
    Hammers: Fear, O Little Hunter—this is Fear!

                                        RUDYARD KIPLING

SHERWOOD in the twilight, is Robin Hood awake?
Grey and ghostly shadows are gliding through the brake,
Shadows of the dappled deer, dreaming of the morn,
Dreaming of a shadowy man that winds a shadowy horn.

Robin Hood is here again: all his merry thieves
Hear a ghostly bugle-note shivering through the leaves,
Calling as he used to call, faint and far away,
In Sherwood, in Sherwood, about the break of day.

Merry, merry England has kissed the lips of June:
All the wings of fairyland were here beneath the moon,
Like a flight of rose-leaves fluttering in a mist
Of opal and ruby and pearl and amethyst.

Merry, merry England is waking as of old,
With eyes of blither hazel and hair of brighter gold:
For Robin Hood is here again beneath the bursting spray
In Sherwood, in Sherwood, about the break of day.

Love is in the greenwood building him a house
Of wild rose and hawthorn and honeysuckle boughs:
Love is in the greenwood, dawn is in the skies,
And Marian is waiting with a glory in her eyes.

Hark! the dazzled laverock climbs the golden steep!
Marian is waiting: is Robin Hood asleep?
Round the fairy grass-rings frolic elf and fay,
In Sherwood, in Sherwood, about the break of day.

Oberon, Oberon, rake away the gold,
Rake away the red leaves, roll away the mould,
Rake away the gold leaves, roll away the red,
And wake Will Scarlett from his leafy forest bed.

Friar Tuck and Little John are riding down together,
With quarterstaff and drinking-can and grey goose feather.
The dead are coming back again, the years are rolled away
In Sherwood, in Sherwood, about the break of day.

Softly over Sherwood the south wind blows.
All the heart of England hid in every rose
Hears across the greenwood the sunny whisper leap,
Sherwood in the red dawn, is Robin Hood asleep?

Hark, the voice of England wakes him as of old
And, shattering the silence with a cry of brighter gold,
Bugles in the greenwood echo from the steep,
Sherwood in the red dawn, is Robin Hood asleep?

Where the deer are gliding down the shadowy glen
All across the glades of fern he calls his merry men—
Doublets of the Lincoln green glancing through the may
In Sherwood, in Sherwood, about the break of day—

Calls them and they answer—from aisles of oak and ash
Rings the *Follow! Follow!* and the boughs begin to crash,
The ferns begin to flutter, and the flowers begin to fly,
And through the crimson dawning the robber band goes by.

Robin! Robin! Robin! All his merry thieves
Answer as the bugle-note shivers through the leaves,
Calling as he used to call, faint and far away,
In Sherwood, in Sherwood, about the break of day.

ALFRED NOYES

IF you wake at midnight, and hear a horse's feet,
Don't go drawing back the blind, or looking in the street,
Them that ask no questions isn't told a lie.
Watch the wall, my darling, while the Gentlemen go by!
       Five and twenty ponies,
       Trotting through the dark—
       Brandy for the Parson,
       'Baccy for the Clerk;
       Laces for a lady, letters for a spy,
And watch the wall, my darling, while the Gentlemen go by!

Running round the woodlump if you chance to find
Little barrels, roped and tarred, all full of brandy-wine,
Don't you shout to come and look, nor use 'em for your play.
Put the brishwood back again—and they'll be gone next day!

If you see the stable-door setting open wide;
If you see a tired horse lying down inside;
If your mother mends a coat cut about and tore;
If the lining's wet and warm—don't you ask no more!

If you meet King George's men, dressed in blue and red,
You be careful what you say, and mindful what is said.
If they call you 'pretty maid,' and chuck you 'neath the chin,
Don't you tell where no one is, nor yet where no one's been!

Knocks and footsteps round the house—whistles after dark—
You've no call for running out till the house-dogs bark.
Trusty's here, and *Pincher*'s here, and see how dumb they lie—
They don't fret to follow when the Gentlemen go by!

If you do as you've been told, 'likely there's a chance,
You'll be give a dainty doll, all the way from France,
With a cap of Valenciennes, and a velvet hood—
A present from the Gentlemen, along o' being good!
   Five and twenty ponies,
    Trotting through the dark—
   Brandy for the Parson,
    'Baccy for the Clerk.
Them that asks no questions isn't told a lie—
Watch the wall, my darling, while the Gentlemen go by!
         RUDYARD KIPLING

64   *The Last Buccaneer*

OH, England is a pleasant place for them that's rich and
  high,
But England is a cruel place for such poor folks as I;
And such a port for mariners I ne'er shall see again
As the pleasant Isle of Avès, beside the Spanish main.

There were forty craft in Avès that were both swift and
  stout,
All furnished well with small arms and cannons round about;
And a thousand men in Avès made laws so fair and free
To choose their valiant captains and obey them loyally.

Thence we sailed against the Spaniard with his hoards of
  plate and gold,
Which he wrung with cruel tortures from Indian folk of old;
Likewise the merchant captains, with hearts as hard as
  stone,
Who flog men and keel-haul them, and starve them to the
  bone.

117

Oh, the palms grew high in Avès, and fruits that shone like
    gold,
And the colibris and parrots they were gorgeous to behold;
And the negro maids to Avès from bondage fast did flee,
To welcome gallant sailors, a-sweeping in from sea.

Oh, sweet it was in Avès to hear the landward breeze,
A-swing with good tobacco in a net between the trees,
With a negro lass to fan you, while you listened to the roar
Of the breakers on the reef outside, that never touched the
    shore.

But Scripture saith, an ending to all fine things must be,
So the King's ships sailed on Avès, and quite put down were
    we.
All day we fought like bulldogs, but they burst the booms
    at night;
And I fled in a piragua, sore wounded, from the fight.

Nine days I floated starving, and a negro lass beside,
Till for all I tried to cheer her, the poor young thing she died;
But as I lay a-gasping, a Bristol sail came by,
And brought me home to England here, to beg until I die.

And now I'm old and going—I'm sure I can't tell where:
One comfort is, this world's so hard, I can't be worse off
    there:
If I might but be a sea-dove, I'd fly across the main,
To the pleasant Isle of Avès, to look at it once again.

CHARLES KINGSLEY

The Revenge

At Florés in the Azores Sir Richard Grenville lay,
And a pinnace, like a fluttered bird, came flying from far
away:
'Spanish ships of war at sea! we have sighted fifty-three!'
Then sware Lord Thomas Howard: ''Fore God I am no
coward;
But I cannot meet them here, for my ships are out of gear,
And the half my men are sick. I must fly, but follow quick.
We are six ships of the line; can we fight with fifty-three?'

Then spake Sir Richard Grenville: 'I know you are no
coward;
You fly them for a moment to fight with them again.
But I've ninety men and more that are lying sick ashore.
I should count myself the coward if I left them, my Lord
Howard,
To these Inquisition dogs and the devildoms of Spain.'

So Lord Howard passed away with five ships of war that day,
Till he melted like a cloud in the silent summer heaven;
But Sir Richard bore in hand all his sick men from the land
Very carefully and slow,
Men of Bideford in Devon,
And we laid them on the ballast down below;
For we brought them all aboard,
And they blest him in their pain, that they were not left to
Spain,
To the thumbscrew and the stake, for the glory of the Lord.

He had only a hundred seamen to work the ship and to fight,
And he sailed away from Florés till the Spaniard came in
sight,

With his huge sea-castles heaving upon the weather bow.
'Shall we fight or shall we fly?
Good Sir Richard, tell us now,
For to fight is but to die!
There'll be little of us left by the time this sun be set.'
And Sir Richard said again: 'We be all good English men.
Let us bang these dogs of Seville, the children of the devil,
For I never turned my back upon Don or devil yet.'

Sir Richard spoke and he laughed, and we roared a hurrah,
and so
The little *Revenge* ran on sheer into the heart of the foe,
With her hundred fighters on deck, and her ninety sick
below;
For half their fleet to the right and half to the left were seen,
And the little *Revenge* ran on through the long sea-lane
between.

Thousands of their soldiers looked down from their decks
and laughed,
Thousands of their seamen made mock at the mad little craft
Running on and on, till delayed
By their mountain-like *San Philip* that, of fifteen hundred tons,
And up-shadowing high above us with her yawning tiers of
guns,
Took the breath from our sails, and we stayed.

And while now the great *San Philip* hung above us like a cloud
Whence the thunderbolt will fall
Long and loud,
Four galleons drew away
From the Spanish fleet that day,
And two upon the larboard and two upon the starboard lay,
And the battle thunder broke from them all.

But anon the great *San Philip*, she bethought herself and
went,
Having that within her womb that had left her ill content;
And the rest they came aboard us, and they fought us hand to
hand,
For a dozen times they came with their pikes and mus-
queteers,
And a dozen times we shook 'em off as a dog that shakes
his ears
When he leaps from the water to the land.

And the sun went down, and the stars came out far over
the summer sea,
But never a moment ceased the fight of the one and the
fifty-three.
Ship after ship, the whole night long, their high-built
galleons came,
Ship after ship, the whole night long, with her battle-
thunder and flame;
Ship after ship, the whole night long, drew back with her
dead and her shame.
For some were sunk and many were shattered, and so could
fight us no more—
God of battles, was ever a battle like this in the world before?

For he said, 'Fight on! fight on!'
Though his vessel was all but a wreck;
And it chanced that, when half of the short summer night
was gone,
With a grisly wound to be drest he had left the deck,
But a bullet struck him that was dressing it suddenly dead,
And himself he was wounded again in the side and the head,
And he said, 'Fight on! fight on!'

And the night went down and the sun smiled out far over
    the summer sea,
And the Spanish fleet with broken sides lay round us all in
    a ring;
But they dared not touch us again, for they feared that we
    still could sting,
So they watched what the end would be.

And we had not fought them in vain,
But in perilous plight were we,
Seeing forty of our poor hundred were slain,
And half the rest of us maimed for life
In the crash of the cannonades and the desperate strife;
And the sick men down in the hold were most of them
    stark and cold,
And the pikes were all broken or bent, and the powder was
    all of it spent;
And the masts and the rigging were lying over the side;
But Sir Richard cried in his English pride,
'We have fought such a fight for a day and a night,
As may never be fought again!
We have won great glory, my men!
And a day less or more
At sea or ashore,
We die—does it matter when?
Sink me the ship, Master Gunner—sink her, split her in twain!
Fall into the hands of God, not into the hands of Spain!'

And the gunner said, 'Ay, ay,' but the seamen made reply:
'We have children, we have wives,
And the Lord hath spared our lives.
We will make the Spaniard promise, if we yield, to let us go;
We shall live to fight again and to strike another blow.'
And the lion there lay dying, and they yielded to the foe.

And the stately Spanish men to their flagship bore him then,
Where they laid him by the mast, old Sir Richard caught at
    last,
And they praised him to his face with their courtly foreign
    grace;
But he rose upon their decks, and he cried:
'I have fought for Queen and Faith like a valiant man and
    true;
I have only done my duty as a man is bound to do;
With a joyful spirit I Sir Richard Grenville die!'
And he fell upon their decks, and he died.

And they stared at the dead that had been so valiant and
    true,
And had holden the power and glory of Spain so cheap
That he dared her with one little ship and his English
    few;
Was he devil or man? He was devil for aught they knew,
But they sank his body with honour down into the deep,
And they manned the *Revenge* with a swarthier alien crew,
And away she sailed with her loss and longed for her own;
When a wind from the lands they had ruined awoke from
    sleep,
And the water began to heave and the weather to moan,
And or ever that evening ended a great gale blew,
And a wave like the wave that is raised by an earthquake
    grew,
Till it smote on their hulls and their sails and their masts
    and their flags,
And the whole sea plunged and fell on the shot-shattered
    navy of Spain,
And the little *Revenge* herself went down by the island crags
To be lost evermore in the main.

LORD TENNYSON

'TWAS on the shores that round our coast
  From Deal to Ramsgate span,
That I found alone on a piece of stone
  An elderly naval man.

His hair was weedy, his beard was long,
  And weedy and long was he,
And I heard this wight on the shore recite,
  In a singular minor key:

'Oh, I am a cook and a captain bold,
  And the mate of the *Nancy* brig,
And a bo'sun tight, and a midshipmite,
  And the crew of the captain's gig.'

And he shook his fists and he tore his hair,
  Till I really felt afraid,
For I couldn't help thinking the man had been drinking,
  And so I simply said:

'Oh, elderly man, it's little I know
  Of the duties of men of the sea,
And I'll eat my hand if I understand
  How you can possibly be

At once a cook, and a captain bold,
  And the mate of the *Nancy* brig,
And a bo'sun tight, and a midshipmite,
  And the crew of the captain's gig.'

Then he gave a hitch to his trousers, which
  Is a trick all seamen larn,
And having got rid of a thumping quid,
  He spun his painful yarn:

'Twas in the good ship *Nancy Bell*
  That we sailed to the Indian Sea,
And there on a reef we come to grief,
  Which has often occurred to me.

And pretty nigh all the crew was drowned
  (There was seventy-seven o' soul),
And only ten of the *Nancy*'s men
  Said 'here' to the muster-roll.

There was me and the cook and the captain bold,
  And the mate of the *Nancy* brig,
And the bo'sun tight, and a midshipmite,
  And the crew of the captain's gig.

For a month we'd neither wittles nor drink,
  Till a-hungry we did feel,
So we drawed a lot, and accordin' shot
  The captain for our meal.

The next lot fell to the *Nancy*'s mate,
  And a delicate dish he made;
Then our appetite with the midshipmite
  We seven survivors stayed.

And then we murdered the bo'sun tight,
  And he much resembled pig:
Then we wittled free, did the cook and me,
  On the crew of the captain's gig.

Then only the cook and me was left,
  And the delicate question, 'Which
Of us two goes to the kettle?' arose,
  And we argued it out as sich.

For I loved that cook as a brother, I did,
  And the cook he worshipped me;
But we'd both be blowed if we'd either be stowed
  In the other chap's hold, you see.

'I'll be eat if you dines off me,' says Tom.
  'Yes, that,' says I, 'you'll be,—
I'm boiled if I die, my friend,' quoth I.
  And 'Exactly so,' quoth he.

Says he, 'Dear James, to murder me
  Were a foolish thing to do,
For don't you see that you can't cook *me*,
  While I can—and will—cook *you!*'

So he boils the water, and takes the salt
  And the pepper in portions true
(Which he never forgot), and some chopped shallot,
  And some sage and parsley too.

'Come here,' says he, with a proper pride,
  Which his smiling features tell,
''Twill soothing be if I let you see
  How extremely nice you'll smell.'

And he stirred it round and round and round,
  And he sniffed at the foaming froth;
When I ups with his heels, and smothers his squeals
  In the scum of the boiling broth.

And I eat that cook in a week or less,
  And—as I eating be
The last of his chops, why, I almost drops,
  For a vessel in sight I see.

And I never larf, and I never smile,
  And I never lark or play,
But sit and croak, and a single joke
  I have,—which is to say:

Oh, I am a cook and a captain bold,
  And the mate of the *Nancy* brig,
And a bo'sun tight, and a midshipmite,
  And the crew of the captain's gig.'
                                W. S. GILBERT

67   *Sir Patrick Spens*

I. THE SAILING

THE king sits in Dunfermline town
  Drinking the blude-red wine;
'O whare will I get a skeely skipper
  To sail this new ship o' mine?'

O up and spak an eldern knight,
  Sat at the king's right knee;
'Sir Patrick Spens is the best sailor
  That ever sail'd the sea.'

Our king has written a braid letter,
  And seal'd it with his hand,
And sent it to Sir Patrick Spens,
  Was walking on the strand.

'To Noroway, to Noroway,
  To Noroway o'er the faem;
The king's daughter o' Noroway,
  'Tis thou must bring her hame.'

The first word that Sir Patrick read
  So loud, loud laugh'd he;
The neist word that Sir Patrick read
  The tear blinded his e'e.

'O wha is this has done this deed
  And tauld the king o' me,
To send us out, at this time o' year,
  To sail upon the sea?

'Be it wind, be it weet, be it hail, be it sleet,
  Our ship must sail the faem;
The king's daughter o' Noroway,
  'Tis we must fetch her hame.'

They hoysèd their sails on Monenday morn
  Wi' a' the speed they may;
They hae landed in Noroway
  Upon a Wodensday.

II. THE RETURN

'Mak' ready, mak' ready, my merry men a'!
  Our gude ship sails the morn.'
'Now ever alack, my master dear,
  I fear a deadly storm.

'I saw the new moon late yestreen
  Wi' the auld moon in her arm;
And if we gang to sea, master,
  I fear we'll come to harm.'

They hadna sail'd a league, a league,
  A league but barely three,
When the lift grew dark, and the wind blew loud,
  And gurly grew the sea.

The ankers brak, and the topmast lap,
   It was sic a deadly storm:
And the waves cam' owre the broken ship
   Till a' her sides were torn.

'O whare will I get a gude sailor
   To tak' my helm in hand,
Till I get up to the tall topmast,
   To see if I can spy land?'—

'O here am I, a sailor gude,
   To tak' the helm in hand,
Till you go up to the tall topmast,
   But I fear you'll ne'er spy land.'

He hadna gone a step, a step,
   A step but barely ane,
When a bout flew out of our goodly ship,
   And the saut sea it cam' in.

'Go fetch a web o' the silken claith,
   Another o' the twine,
And wap them into our ship's side,
   And let nae the sea come in.'

They fetch'd a web o' the silken claith,
   Another o' the twine,
And they wapp'd them round the gude ship's side,
   But still the sea cam' in.

O laith, laith were our gude Scots lords
   To weet their cork-heeled shoon!
But lang or a' the play was play'd,
   They wat their hats aboon.

And mony was the feather-bed
   That flattered on the faem;
And mony was the gude lord's son
   That never mair cam' hame.

O lang, lang may the ladies sit,
   Wi' their fans into their hand,
Before they see Sir Patrick Spens
   Come sailing to the strand!

And lang, lang may the maidens sit,
   Wi' their gowd kaims in their hair,
A-waiting for their ain dear loves!
   For them they'll see nae mair.

Half owre, half owre to Aberdour,
   'Tis fifty fathom deep,
And there lies gude Sir Patrick Spens
   Wi' the Scots lords at his feet.

BALLAD

68   *The Forsaken Merman*

COME, dear children, let us away;
Down and away below.
Now my brothers call from the bay;
Now the great winds shorewards blow;
Now the salt tides seawards flow;
Now the wild white horses play,
Champ and chafe and toss in the spray.
    Children dear, let us away.
    This way, this way.

Call her once before you go.
        Call once yet.
In a voice that she will know:
        'Margaret! Margaret!'
Children's voices should be dear
(Call once more) to a mother's ear;
Children's voices, wild with pain—
        Surely she will come again.
Call her once and come away,
            This way, this way.
'Mother dear, we cannot stay.'
The wild white horses foam and fret.
        Margaret! Margaret!

Come, dear children, come away down.
        Call no more.
One last look at the white-walled town,
And the little grey church on the windy shore,
        Then come down.
She will not come though you call all day.
        Come away, come away.

Children dear, was it yesterday
We heard the sweet bells over the bay?
In the caverns where we lay,
Through the surf and through the swell,
The far-off sound of a silver bell?
Sand-strewn caverns, cool and deep,
Where the winds are all asleep;
Where the spent lights quiver and gleam;
Where the salt weed sways in the stream;
Where the sea-beasts, ranged all round,
Feed in the ooze of their pasture-ground;
Where the sea-snakes coil and twine,
Dry their mail and bask in the brine;

Where great whales come sailing by,
Sail and sail, with unshut eye,
Round the world for ever and aye?
When did music come this way?
Children dear, was it yesterday?

Children dear, was it yesterday
(Call yet once) that she went away?
Once she sate with you and me,
On a red gold throne in the heart of the sea,
And the youngest sate on her knee.
She combed its bright hair, and she tended it well,
When down swung the sound of the far-off bell.
She sighed, she looked up through the clear green sea;
She said: 'I must go, for my kinsfolk pray
In the little grey church on the shore to-day.
'Twill be Easter-time in the world—ah me!
And I lose my poor soul, merman! here with thee.'
I said: 'Go up, dear heart, through the waves;
Say thy prayer, and come back to the kind sea-caves!'
She smiled, she went up through the surf in the bay.
Children dear, was it yesterday?

Children dear, were we long alone?
'The sea grows stormy, the little ones moan;
Long prayers,' I said, 'in the world they say;
Come!' I said; and we rose through the surf in the bay.
We went up the beach, by the sandy down
Where the sea-stocks bloom, to the white-walled town;
Through the narrow paved streets, where all was still,
To the little grey church on the windy hill.
From the church came a murmur of folk at their prayers,
But we stood without in the cold blowing airs.
We climbed on the graves, on the stones, worn with rains,
And we gazed up the aisle through the small leaded panes.

She sate by the pillar; we saw her clear:
'Margaret, hist! come quick, we are here.
Dear heart,' I said, 'we are long alone.
The sea grows stormy, the little ones moan.'
But, ah, she gave me never a look,
For her eyes were sealed to the holy book.
Loud prays the priest; shut stands the door.
Come away, children, call no more.
Come away, come down, call no more.

        Down, down, down.
        Down to the depths of the sea.
She sits at her wheel in the humming town,
        Singing most joyfully.
Hark, what she sings: 'O joy, O joy,
For the humming street, and the child with its toy,
For the priest, and the bell, and the holy well—
        For the wheel where I spun,
        And the blessed light of the sun.'
And so she sings her fill,
Singing most joyfully,
Till the shuttle falls from her hand,
And the whizzing wheel stands still.
She steals to the window, and looks at the sand;
And over the sand at the sea;
And her eyes are set in a stare;
And anon there breaks a sigh,
And anon there drops a tear,
From a sorrow-clouded eye,
And a heart sorrow-laden,
A long, long sigh;
For the cold strange eyes of a little Mermaiden,
And the gleam of her golden hair.

Come away, away, children;
Come, children, come down!
The hoarse wind blows colder;
Lights shine in the town.
She will start from her slumber
When gusts shake the door;
She will hear the winds howling,
Will hear the waves roar.
We shall see, while above us
The waves roar and whirl,
A ceiling of amber,
A pavement of pearl,
Singing: 'Here came a mortal,
But faithless was she!
And alone dwell for ever
The kings of the sea.'

But, children, at midnight,
When soft the winds blow,
When clear falls the moonlight,
When spring-tides are low;
When sweet airs come seaward
From heaths starred with broom,
And high rocks throw mildly
On the blanched sands a gloom;
Up the still, glistening beaches,
Up the creeks we will hie,
Over banks of bright seaweed
The ebb-tide leaves dry.
We will gaze, from the sand-hills,
At the white, sleeping town;
At the church on the hill-side—
    And then come back down.

Singing, 'There dwells a loved one,
But cruel is she.
She left lonely for ever
The kings of the sea.'

MATTHEW ARNOLD

69 *Song*

A WIDOW bird sate mourning for her love
  Upon a wintry bough;
The frozen wind crept on above,
  The freezing stream below.

There was no leaf upon the forest bare,
  No flower upon the ground,
And little motion in the air
  Except the mill-wheel's sound.

P. B. SHELLEY

70 *The Lady of Shalott*

PART I

ON either side the river lie
Long fields of barley and of rye,
That clothe the wold and meet the sky;
And thro' the field the road runs by
     To many-tower'd Camelot;
And up and down the people go,
Gazing where the lilies blow
Round an island there below,
     The island of Shalott.

Willows whiten, aspens quiver,
Little breezes dusk and shiver
Thro' the wave that runs for ever
By the island in the river
  Flowing down to Camelot.
Four grey walls, and four grey towers,
Overlook a space of flowers,
And the silent isle imbowers
  The Lady of Shalott.

By the margin, willow-veil'd,
Slide the heavy barges trail'd
By slow horses; and unhail'd
The shallop flitteth silken-sail'd
  Skimming down to Camelot;
But who hath seen her wave her hand?
Or at the casement seen her stand?
Or is she known in all the land,
  The Lady of Shalott?

Only reapers, reaping early
In among the bearded barley,
Hear a song that echoes cheerly
From the river winding clearly,
  Down to tower'd Camelot:
And by the moon the reaper weary,
Piling sheaves in uplands airy,
Listening, whispers "Tis the fairy
  Lady of Shalott.'

PART II

There she weaves by night and day
A magic web with colours gay.

She has heard a whisper say,
A curse is on her if she stay
     To look down to Camelot.
She knows not what the curse may be,
And so she weaveth steadily,
And little other care hath she,
     The Lady of Shalott.

And moving thro' a mirror clear
That hangs before her all the year,
Shadows of the world appear.
There she sees the highway near
     Winding down to Camelot:
There the river eddy whirls,
And there the surly village-churls,
And the red-cloaks of market girls,
     Pass onward from Shalott.

Sometimes a troop of damsels glad,
An abbot on an ambling pad,
Sometimes a curly shepherd-lad,
Or long-hair'd page in crimson clad,
     Goes by to tower'd Camelot;
And sometimes thro' the mirror blue
The knights come riding two and two:
She hath no loyal knight and true,
     The Lady of Shalott.

But in her web she still delights
To weave the mirror's magic sights,
For often thro' the silent nights
A funeral, with plumes and lights,
     And music, went to Camelot:

Or when the moon was overhead,
Came two young lovers lately wed;
'I am half sick of shadows,' said
    The Lady of Shalott.

PART III

A bow-shot from her bower-eaves,
He rode between the barley-sheaves,
The sun came dazzling thro' the leaves,
And flamed upon the brazen greaves
        Of bold Sir Lancelot.
A red-cross knight for ever kneel'd
To a lady in his shield,
That sparkled on the yellow field,
        Beside remote Shalott.

The gemmy bridle glitter'd free,
Like to some branch of stars we see
Hung in the golden Galaxy.
The bridle bells rang merrily
        As he rode down to Camelot:
And from his blazon'd baldric slung
A mighty silver bugle hung,
And as he rode his armour rung,
        Beside remote Shalott.

All in the blue unclouded weather
Thick-jewell'd shone the saddle-leather,
The helmet and the helmet-feather
Burn'd like one burning flame together,
        As he rode down to Camelot.

As often thro' the purple night,
Below the starry clusters bright,
Some bearded meteor, trailing light,
    Moves over still Shalott.

His broad clear brow in sunlight glow'd;
On burnish'd hooves his war-horse trode;
From underneath his helmet flow'd
His coal-black curls as on he rode,
    As he rode down to Camelot.
From the bank and from the river
He flash'd into the crystal mirror,
'Tirra lirra,' by the river
    Sang Sir Lancelot.

She left the web, she left the loom,
She made three paces thro' the room,
She saw the water-lily bloom,
She saw the helmet and the plume,
    She look'd down to Camelot.
Out flew the web and floated wide;
The mirror crack'd from side to side;
'The curse is come upon me,' cried
    The Lady of Shalott.

PART IV

In the stormy east-wind straining,
The pale yellow woods were waning,
The broad stream in his banks complaining,
Heavily the low sky raining
    Over tower'd Camelot;

Down she came and found a boat
Beneath a willow left afloat,
And round about the prow she wrote
    The Lady of Shalott.

And down the river's dim expanse—
Like some bold seër in a trance,
Seeing all his own mischance—
With a glassy countenance
    Did she look to Camelot.
And at the closing of the day
She loosed the chain, and down she lay;
The broad stream bore her far away,
    The Lady of Shalott.

Lying, robed in snowy white
That loosely flew to left and right—
The leaves upon her falling light—
Thro' the noises of the night
    She floated down to Camelot:
And as the boat-head wound along
The willowy hills and fields among,
They heard her singing her last song,
    The Lady of Shalott.

Heard a carol, mournful, holy,
Chanted loudly, chanted lowly,
Till her blood was frozen slowly,
And her eyes were darken'd wholly,
    Turn'd to tower'd Camelot.
For ere she reach'd upon the tide
The first house by the water-side,
Singing in her song she died,
    The Lady of Shalott.

Under tower and balcony,
By garden-wall and gallery,
A gleaming shape she floated by,
Dead-pale between the houses high,
    Silent into Camelot.
Out upon the wharfs they came,
Knight and burgher, lord and dame,
And round the prow they read her name,
    The Lady of Shalott.

Who is this? and what is here?
And in the lighted palace near
Died the sound of royal cheer;
And they cross'd themselves for fear,
    All the knights at Camelot;
But Lancelot mused a little space;
He said, 'She has a lovely face;
God in His mercy lend her grace
    The Lady of Shalott.'

LORD TENNYSON

71   *Lochinvar*

O, YOUNG Lochinvar is come out of the west,
Through all the wide border his steed was the best;
And save his good broadsword, he weapons had none,
He rode all unarm'd, and he rode all alone.
So faithful in love, and so dauntless in war,
There never was knight like the young Lochinvar.

He staid not for brake, and he stopp'd not for stone,
He swam the Eske river where ford there was none;
But ere he alighted at Netherby gate,
The bride had consented, the gallant came late;
For a laggard in love, and a dastard in war,
Was to wed the fair Ellen of brave Lochinvar.

So boldly he enter'd the Netherby Hall,
Among bride's-men, and kinsmen, and brothers, and all:
Then spoke the bride's father, his hand on his sword,
(For the poor craven bridegroom said never a word),
'O come ye in peace here, or come ye in war,
Or to dance at our bridal, young Lord Lochinvar?'

'I long woo'd your daughter, my suit you denied;—
Love swells like the Solway, but ebbs like its tide—
And now I am come, with this lost love of mine,
To lead but one measure, drink one cup of wine.
There are maidens in Scotland more lovely by far,
That would gladly be bride to the young Lochinvar.'

The bride kiss'd the goblet: the knight took it up,
He quaff'd off the wine, and he threw down the cup.
She look'd down to blush, and she look'd up to sigh,
With a smile on her lips, and a tear in her eye.
He took her soft hand, ere her mother could bar,—
'Now tread we a measure!' said young Lochinvar.

So stately his form, and so lovely her face,
That never a hall such a galliard did grace;
While her mother did fret, and her father did fume,
And the bridegroom stood dangling his bonnet and plume;
And the bride-maidens whisper'd, ''Twere better by far
To have match'd our fair cousin with young Lochinvar.'

One touch to her hand, and one word in her ear,
When they reached the hall-door, and the charger stood
  near;
So light to the croupe the fair lady he swung,
So light to the saddle before her he sprung;
'She is won! we are gone! over bank, bush, and scaur;
They'll have fleet steeds that follow,' quoth young Lochin-
  var.

There was mounting 'mong Græmes of the Netherby clan;
Forsters, Fenwicks, and Musgraves, they rode and they ran;
There was racing and chasing on Cannobie Lee,
But the lost bride of Netherby ne'er did they see.
So daring in love, and so dauntless in war,
Have ye e'er heard of gallant like young Lochinvar?

SIR W. SCOTT

72   Gillespie

RIDING at dawn, riding alone,
 Gillespie left the town behind;
Before he turned by the Westward road
 A horseman crossed him, staggering blind.

'The Devil's abroad in false Vellore,
 The Devil that stabs by night,' he said,
'Women and children, rank and file,
 Dying and dead, dying and dead.'

Without a word, without a groan,
 Sudden and swift Gillespie turned,
The blood roared in his ears like fire,
 Like fire the road beneath him burned.

He thundered back to Arcot gate,
  He thundered up through Arcot town,
Before he thought a second thought
  In the barrack yard he lighted down.

'Trumpeter, sound for the Light Dragoons,
  Sound to saddle and spur,' he said;
'He that is ready may ride with me,
  And he that can may ride ahead.'

Fierce and fain, fierce and fain,
  Behind him went the troopers grim,
They rode as ride the Light Dragoons
  But never a man could ride with him.

Their rowels ripped their horses' sides,
  Their hearts were red with a deeper goad,
But ever alone before them all
  Gillespie rode, Gillespie rode.

Alone he came to false Vellore,
  The walls were lined, the gates were barred;
Alone he walked where the bullets bit,
  And called above to the Sergeant's Guard.

'Sergeant, Sergeant, over the gate,
  Where are your officers all?' he said;
Heavily came the Sergeant's voice,
  'There are two living and forty dead.'

'A rope, a rope,' Gillespie cried:
  They bound their belts to serve his need;
There was not a rebel behind the wall
  But laid his barrel and drew his bead.

There was not a rebel among them all
    But pulled his trigger and cursed his aim,
For lightly swung and rightly swung
    Over the gate Gillespie came.

He dressed the line, he led the charge,
    They swept the wall like a stream in spate,
And roaring over the roar they heard
    The galloper guns that burst the gate.

Fierce and fain, fierce and fain,
    The troopers rode the reeking flight:
The very stones remember still
    The end of them that stab by night.

They've kept the tale a hundred years,
    They'll keep the tale a hundred more:
Riding at dawn, riding alone,
    Gillespie came to false Vellore.

                        SIR HENRY NEWBOLT

73   *'How they brought the good news
            from Ghent to Aix'*

I SPRANG to the stirrup, and Joris, and he;
I galloped, Dirck galloped, we galloped all three;
'Good speed!' cried the watch, as the gate-bolts undrew;
'Speed!' echoed the wall to us galloping through;
Behind shut the postern, the lights sank to rest,
And into the midnight we galloped abreast.

Not a word to each other; we kept the great pace
Neck by neck, stride by stride, never changing our place;
I turned in my saddle and made its girths tight,
Then shortened each stirrup, and set the pique right,
Rebuckled the cheek-strap, chained slacker the bit,
Nor galloped less steadily Roland a whit.

'Twas moonset at starting; but while we drew near
Lokeren, the cocks crew and twilight dawned clear;
At Boom, a great yellow star came out to see;
At Duffeld, 'twas morning as plain as could be;
And from Mecheln church-steeple we heard the half-chime,
So, Joris broke silence with, 'yet there is time!'

At Aershot, up leaped of a sudden the sun,
And against him the cattle stood black every one,
To stare thro' the mist at us galloping past,
And I saw my stout galloper Roland at last,
With resolute shoulders, each butting away
The haze, as some bluff river headland its spray:

And his low head and crest, just one sharp ear bent back
For my voice, and the other pricked out on his track;
And one eye's black intelligence,—ever that glance
O'er its white edge at me, his own master, askance!
And the thick heavy spume-flakes which aye and anon
His fierce lips shook upwards in galloping on.

By Hasselt, Dirck groaned; and cried Joris, 'Stay spur!
'Your Roos galloped bravely, the fault's not in her,
'We'll remember at Aix'—for one heard the quick wheeze
Of her chest, saw the stretched neck and staggering knees,
And sunk tail, and horrible heave of the flank,
As down on her haunches she shuddered and sank.

So, we were left galloping, Joris and I,
Past Looz and past Tongres, no cloud in the sky;
The broad sun above laughed a pitiless laugh,
'Neath our feet broke the brittle bright stubble like chaff;
Till over by Dalhem a dome-spire sprang white,
And 'Gallop,' gasped Joris, 'for Aix is in sight!'

'How they'll greet us!'—and all in a moment his roan
Rolled neck and croup over, lay dead as a stone;
And there was my Roland to bear the whole weight
Of the news which alone could save Aix from her fate,
With his nostrils like pits full of blood to the brim,
And with circles of red for his eye-sockets' rim.

Then I cast loose my buffcoat, each holster let fall,
Shook off both my jack-boots, let go belt and all,
Stood up in the stirrup, leaned, patted his ear,
Called my Roland his pet-name, my horse without peer;
Clapped my hands, laughed and sang, any noise, bad or good,
Till at length into Aix Roland galloped and stood.

And all I remember is—friends flocking round
As I sat with his head 'twixt my knees on the ground;
And no voice but was praising this Roland of mine,
As I poured down his throat our last measure of wine,
Which (the burgesses voted by common consent)
Was no more than his due who brought good news from
    Ghent.

ROBERT BROWNING

A GOOD sword and a trusty hand!
  A merry heart and true!
King James's men shall understand
  What Cornish lads can do.

And have they fixed the where and when?
  And shall Trelawny die?
Here's twenty thousand Cornish men
  Will know the reason why!

Out spake their captain brave and bold,
  A merry wight was he:
'If London Tower were Michael's hold,
  We'll set Trelawny free!

'We'll cross the Tamar, land to land,
  The Severn is no stay,—
With 'one and all,' and hand in hand,
  And who shall bid us nay?

'And when we come to London Wall,
  A pleasant sight to view,
Come forth! Come forth, ye cowards all,
  Here's men as good as you.

'Trelawny he's in keep and hold
  Trelawny he may die;—
But here's twenty thousand Cornish bold
  Will know the reason why!'

R. S. HAWKER

The Destruction of Sennacherib

THE Assyrian came down like the wolf on the fold,
And his cohorts were gleaming in purple and gold;
And the sheen of their spears was like stars on the sea,
When the blue wave rolls nightly on deep Galilee.

Like the leaves of the forest when Summer is green,
That host with their banners, at sunset were seen:
Like the leaves of the forest when Autumn hath blown,
That host on the morrow lay withered and strown.

For the Angel of Death spread his wings on the blast,
And breathed in the face of the foe as he passed;
And the eyes of the sleepers waxed deadly and chill,
And their hearts but once heaved, and for ever grew still!

And there lay the steed with his nostril all wide,
But through it there rolled not the breath of his pride:
And the foam of his gasping lay white on the turf,
And cold as the spray of the rock-beating surf.

And there lay the rider distorted and pale,
With the dew on his brow, and the rust on his mail;
And the tents were all silent, the banners alone,
The lances unlifted, the trumpets unblown.

And the widows of Ashur are loud in their wail,
And the idols are broke in the temple of Baal;
And the might of the Gentile, unsmote by the sword,
Hath melted like snow in the glance of the Lord!

LORD BYRON

A Negro's interpretation of the Bible Story

DARIUS the Mede was a king and a wonder.
His eye was proud, and his voice was thunder.
He kept bad lions in a monstrous den.
He fed up the lions on Christian men.

Daniel was the chief hired man of the land.
He stirred up the jazz in the palace band.
He whitewashed the cellar. He shovelled in the coal.
And Daniel kept a-praying: 'Lord, save my soul.'
Daniel kept a-praying: 'Lord, save my soul.'
Daniel kept a-praying: 'Lord, save my soul.'

Daniel was the butler, swagger and swell.
He ran upstairs. He answered the bell.
And *he* would let in whoever came a-calling
Saints so holy, scamps so appalling.
'Old man Ahab leaves his card.
Elisha and the bears are a-waiting in the yard.
Here comes Pharaoh and his snakes a-calling.
Here comes Cain and his wife a-calling.
Shadrach, Meshach and Abednego for tea.
Here comes Jonah and the whale,
And the *Sea!*
Here comes St. Peter and his fishing-pole.
Here comes Judas and his silver a-calling,
Here comes old Beelzebub a-calling.'
And Daniel kept a-praying: 'Lord, save my soul.'
Daniel kept a-praying: 'Lord, save my soul.'
Daniel kept a-praying: 'Lord, save my soul.'

His sweetheart and his mother were Christians and meek.
They washed and ironed for Darius every week.
One Thursday he met them at the door:
Paid them as usual, but acted sore.
He said: 'Your Daniel is a dead little pigeon.
He's a good hard worker, but he talks religion.'
And he showed them Daniel in the lion's cage.
Daniel standing quietly, the lions in a rage.

His good old mother cried:—
'Lord, save him.'
And Daniel's tender sweetheart cried:—
'Lord, save him.'
And she was a golden lily in the dew.
And she was as sweet as an apple on the tree.
And she was as fine as a melon in the corn-field,
Gliding and lovely as a ship on the sea,
Gliding and lovely as a ship on the sea.

And she prayed to the Lord:—
'*Send* Gabriel. *Send* Gabriel.'

King Darius said to the lions:—
'Bite Daniel. Bite Daniel.
Bite him. Bite him. Bite him.'

Thus roared the lions:—
'We want Daniel, Daniel, Daniel,
We want Daniel, Daniel, Daniel.
Grrrrrrrrrrrrrrrrr
Grrrrrrrrrrrrrrrrrr.'

And Daniel did not frown,
Daniel did not cry.
He kept on looking at the sky.

And the Lord said to Gabriel:—
'Go chain the lions down,
Go chain the lions down,
Go chain the lions down,
Go chain the lions down.'
And *Gabriel* chained the lions,
And *Gabriel* chained the lions,
And *Gabriel* chained the lions,
And Daniel got out of the den,
And Daniel got out of the den,
And Daniel got out of the den.
And Darius said: 'You're a Christian child,'
Darius said: 'You're a Christian child,'
Darius said: 'You're a Christian child,'
And gave him his job again,
And gave him his job again,
And gave him his job again.

VACHEL LINDSAY

77   *The Heavens Declare*

THE heavens declare the glory of God; and the firmament sheweth his handywork.

Day unto day uttereth speech, and night unto night sheweth knowledge.

There is no speech nor language, where their voice is not heard.

Their line is gone out through all the earth, and their words to the end of the world. In them hath he set a tabernacle for the sun,

Which is as a bridegroom coming out of his chamber, and rejoiceth as a strong man to run a race.

152

His going forth is from the end of the heaven, and his circuit unto the ends of it: and there is nothing hid from the heat thereof.

The law of the Lord is perfect, converting the soul: the testimony of the Lord is sure, making wise the simple.

The statutes of the Lord are right, rejoicing the heart: the commandment of the Lord is pure, enlightening the eyes.

The fear of the Lord is clean, enduring for ever; the judgments of the Lord are true and righteous altogether.

More to be desired are they than gold, yea, than much fine gold: sweeter also than honey and the honeycomb.

Moreover by them is thy servant warned: and in keeping of them there is great reward.

Who can understand his errors? cleanse thou me from secret faults.

Keep back thy servant also from presumptuous sins; let them not have dominion over me: then shall I be upright, and I shall be innocent from the great transgression.

Let the words of my mouth, and the meditation of my heart, be acceptable in thy sight, O Lord, my strength and my redeemer.

THE BIBLE

78 *Leisure*

WHAT is this life if, full of care,
We have no time to stand and stare?
No time to stand beneath the boughs
And stare as long as sheep or cows:
No time to see, when woods we pass,
Where squirrels hide their nuts in grass:

No time to see, in broad daylight,
Streams full of stars, like stars at night:
No time to turn at Beauty's glance,
And watch her feet, how they can dance:
No time to wait till her mouth can
Enrich that smile her eyes began?
A poor life this if, full of care,
We have no time to stand and stare.

W. H. DAVIES

79   *The Reverie of Poor Susan*

AT the corner of Wood Street, when daylight appears,
Hangs a Thrush that sings loud, it has sung for three years:
Poor Susan has pass'd by the spot, and has heard
In the silence of morning the song of the bird.

'Tis a note of enchantment; what ails her? She sees
A mountain ascending, a vision of trees;
Bright volumes of vapour through Lothbury glide,
And a river flows on through the vale of Cheapside.

Green pastures she views in the midst of the dale,
Down which she so often has tripp'd with her pail;
And a single small cottage, a nest like a dove's,
The one only dwelling on earth that she loves.

She looks, and her heart is in heaven: but they fade,
The mist and the river, the hill and the shade;
The stream will not flow, and the hill will not rise,
And the colours have all pass'd away from her eyes!

W. WORDSWORTH

I WANDERED lonely as a cloud
  That floats on high o'er vales and hills,
When all at once I saw a crowd,
  A host, of golden daffodils;
Beside the lake, beneath the trees,
Fluttering and dancing in the breeze.

Continuous as the stars that shine
  And twinkle on the milky way,
They stretched in never-ending line
  Along the margin of a bay:
Ten thousand saw I at a glance,
Tossing their heads in sprightly dance.

The waves beside them danced; but they
  Out-did the sparkling waves in glee:
A Poet could not but be gay,
  In such a jocund company:
I gazed—and gazed—but little thought
What wealth the show to me had brought:

For oft, when on my couch I lie
  In vacant or in pensive mood,
They flash upon that inward eye
  Which is the bliss of solitude;
And then my heart with pleasure fills,
And dances with the daffodils.

               W. WORDSWORTH

You spotted snakes with double tongue,
  Thorny hedgehogs, be not seen;
Newts and blind-worms, do no wrong:
  Come not near our fairy queen.

    Philomel, with melody,
    Sing in our sweet lullaby;
    Lulla, lulla, lullaby; lulla, lulla, lullaby!
      Never harm,
      Nor spell, nor charm,
    Come our lovely lady nigh:
    So, good night, with lullaby.

Weaving spiders, come not here;
  Hence, you long-legg'd spinners, hence!
Beetles black, approach not near;
  Worm nor snail, do no offence.

    Philomel, with melody,
    Sing in our sweet lullaby;
    Lulla, lulla, lullaby; lulla, lulla, lullaby!
      Never harm,
      Nor spell nor charm,
    Come our lovely lady nigh;
    So, good night, with lullaby!
                              W. SHAKESPEARE

Sweet and Low

SWEET and low, sweet and low,
  Wind of the western sea,
Low, low, breathe and blow,
  Wind of the western sea!
Over the rolling waters go,
Come from the dying moon, and blow,
  Blow him again to me;
While my little one, while my pretty one, sleeps.

Sleep and rest, sleep and rest,
  Father will come to thee soon;
Rest, rest, on mother's breast,
  Father will come to thee soon;
Father will come to his babe in the nest,
Silver sails all out of the west
  Under the silver moon:
Sleep, my little one, sleep, my pretty one, sleep.

LORD TENNYSON

Cherry-ripe

CHERRY-RIPE, ripe, ripe, I cry,
Full and fair ones; come and buy.
If so be you ask me where
They do grow, I answer: There
Where my Julia's lips do smile;
There's the land, or cherry-isle,
Whose plantations fully show
All the year where cherries grow.

R. HERRICK

The Poplar Field

THE poplars are fell'd; farewell to the shade
And the whispering sound of the cool colonnade,
The winds play no longer and sing in the leaves,
Nor Ouse on his bosom their image receives.

Twelve years have elapsed since I first took a view
Of my favourite field, and the bank where they grew,
And now in the grass behold they are laid,
And the tree is my seat that once lent me a shade.

The blackbird has fled to another retreat,
Where the hazels afford him a screen from the heat,
And the scene where his melody charm'd me before,
Resounds with his sweet-flowing ditty no more.

My fugitive years are all hasting away,
And I must ere long lie as lowly as they,
With a turf on my breast, and a stone at my head,
Ere another such grove shall arise in its stead.

'Tis a sight to engage me, if anything can,
To muse on the perishing pleasures of man;
Though his life be a dream, his enjoyments, I see,
Have a being less durable even than he.

W. COWPER

85   *Time, You Old Gipsy Man*

TIME, you old gipsy man,
    Will you not stay,
Put up your caravan
    Just for one day?

All things I'll give you,
Will you be my guest,
Bells for your jennet
Of silver the best,
Goldsmiths shall beat you
A great golden ring,
Peacocks shall bow to you,
Little boys sing,
Oh, and sweet girls will
Festoon you with may,
Time, you old gipsy,
Why hasten away?

Last week in Babylon,
Last night in Rome,
Morning, and in the crush
Under Paul's dome;
Under Paul's dial
You tighten your rein—
Only a moment,
And off once again;
Off to some city
Now blind in the womb,
Off to another
Ere that's in the tomb.

Time, you old gipsy man,
  Will you not stay,
Put up your caravan
  Just for one day?

RALPH HODGSON

159

THE sun was shining on the sea,
  Shining with all his might:
He did his very best to make
  The billows smooth and bright—
And this was odd, because it was
  The middle of the night.

The moon was shining sulkily,
  Because she thought the sun
Had got no business to be there
  After the day was done—
'It's very rude of him,' she said,
  'To come and spoil the fun!'

The sea was wet as wet could be,
  The sands were dry as dry.
You could not see a cloud, because
  No cloud was in the sky:
No birds were flying overhead—
  There were no birds to fly.

The Walrus and the Carpenter
  Were walking close at hand;
They wept like anything to see
  Such quantities of sand:
'If this were only cleared away,'
  They said, 'It *would* be grand!'

'If seven maids with seven mops
  Swept it for half a year,
Do you suppose,' the Walrus said,
  'That they could get it clear?'
'I doubt it,' said the Carpenter,
  And shed a bitter tear.

'O Oysters, come and walk with us!'
   The Walrus did beseech.
'A pleasant walk, a pleasant talk,
   Along the briny beach:
We cannot do with more than four,
   To give a hand to each.'

The eldest Oyster looked at him,
   But never a word he said:
The eldest Oyster winked his eye,
   And shook his heavy head—
Meaning to say he did not choose
   To leave the oyster-bed.

But four young Oysters hurried up,
   All eager for the treat:
Their coats were brushed, their faces washed,
   Their shoes were clean and neat—
And this was odd, because, you know,
   They hadn't any feet.

Four other Oysters followed them,
   And yet another four;
And thick and fast they came at last,
   And more, and more, and more—
All hopping through the frothy waves,
   And scrambling to the shore.

The Walrus and the Carpenter
   Walked on a mile or so,
And then they rested on a rock
   Conveniently low:
And all the little Oysters stood
   And waited in a row.

'The time has come,' the Walrus said,
  'To talk of many things:
Of shoes -and ships—and sealing-wax—
  Of cabbages—and kings—
And why the sea is boiling hot—
  And whether pigs have wings.'

'But, wait a bit,' the Oysters cried,
  'Before we have our chat;
For some of us are out of breath,
  And all of us are fat!'
'No hurry!' said the Carpenter,
  They thanked him much for that.

'A loaf of bread,' the Walrus said,
  'Is what we chiefly need:
Pepper and vinegar besides
  Are very good indeed—
Now if you're ready, Oysters dear,
  We can begin to feed.'

'But not on us!' the Oysters cried,
  Turning a little blue,
'After such kindness, that would be
  A dismal thing to do!'
'The night is fine,' the Walrus said,
  'Do you admire the view?

'It was so kind of you to come!
  And you are very nice!'
The Carpenter said nothing but
  'Cut us another slice:
I wish you were not quite so deaf—
  I've had to ask you twice!'

'It seems a shame,' the Walrus said,
  'To play them such a trick,
After we've brought them out so far,
  And made them trot so quick!'
The Carpenter said nothing but
  'The butter's spread too thick!'

'I weep for you,' the Walrus said,
  'I deeply sympathize.'
With sobs and tears he sorted out
  Those of the largest size,
Holding his pocket-handkerchief
  Before his streaming eyes.

'O Oysters,' said the Carpenter,
  'You've had a pleasant run!
Shall we be trotting home again?'
  But answer came there none—
And this was scarcely odd, because
  They'd eaten every one.

LEWIS CARROLL

87   *Lord Randal*

'O, WHERE hae ye been, Lord Randal, my son?
O, where hae ye been, my handsome young man?'—
'I have been to the wild wood; mother, make my bed soon,
For I'm weary wi' hunting, and fain wald lie down.'

'Where gat ye your dinner, Lord Randal, my son?
Where gat ye your dinner, my handsome young man?'—
'I dined wi' my true-love; mother, make my bed soon,
For I'm weary wi' hunting, and fain wald lie down.'

'What gat ye to your dinner, Lord Randal, my son?
What gat ye to your dinner, my handsome young man?'—
'I gat eels boiled in bro'; mother, make my bed soon,
For I'm weary wi' hunting, and fain wald lie down.'

'What became of your bloodhounds, Lord Randal, my son?
'What became of your bloodhounds, my handsome young
    man?'—
'O, they swell'd and they died; mother, make my bed soon,
For I'm weary wi' hunting, and fain wald lie down.'

'O, I fear ye are poison'd, Lord Randal, my son!
O, I fear ye are poison'd, my handsome young man!'—
'O, yes, I am poison'd; mother, make my bed soon,
For I'm sick at the heart, and I fain wald lie down.'

BALLAD

88 *John Barleycorn*

THERE were three kings into the east,
    Three kings both great and high;
And they hae sworn a solemn oath
    John Barleycorn should die.

They took a plough and plough'd him down,
    Put clods upon his head;
And they hae sworn a solemn oath
    John Barleycorn was dead.

But the cheerful Spring came kindly on,
    And show'rs began to fall;
John Barleycorn got up again,
    And sore surpris'd them all.

164

The sultry suns of Summer came,
   And he grew thick and strong;
His head weel arm'd wi' pointed spears,
   That no one should him wrong.

The sober Autumn enter'd mild,
   When he grew wan and pale;
His bending joints and drooping head
   Show'd he began to fail.

His colour sicken'd more and more,
   He faded into age;
And then his enemies began
   To show their deadly rage.

They've ta'en a weapon, long and sharp,
   And cut him by the knee;
Then tied him fast upon a cart,
   Like a rogue for forgerie.

They laid him down upon his back,
   And cudgell'd him full sore;
They hung him up before the storm,
   And turn'd him o'er and o'er.

They fillèd up a darksome pit
   With water to the brim;
They heavèd in John Barleycorn,
   There let him sink or swim.

They laid him out upon the floor,
  To work him further woe:
And still, as signs of life appear'd,
  They toss'd him to and fro.

They wasted o'er a scorching flame
  The marrow of his bones;
But a miller us'd him worst of all—
  He crush'd him 'tween two stones.

And they hae ta'en his very heart's blood,
  And drank it round and round;
And still the more and more they drank,
  Their joy did more abound.

John Barleycorn was a hero bold,
  Of noble enterprise;
For if you do but taste his blood,
  'Twill make your courage rise.

'Twill make a man forget his woe;
  'Twill heighten all his joy;
'Twill make the widow's heart to sing,
  Tho' the tear were in her eye.

Then let us toast John Barleycorn,
  Each man a glass in hand;
And may his great posterity
  Ne'er fail in old Scotland!

ROBERT BURNS

THERE were twa sisters sat in a bour;
  Binnorie, O Binnorie!
There cam a knight to be their wooer,
  By the bonnie milldams o' Binnorie.

He courted the eldest with glove and ring,
But he lo'ed the youngest abune a' thing.

The eldest she was vexed sair,
And sair envied her sister fair.

Upon a morning fair and clear,
She cried upon her sister dear:

'O sister, sister, tak my hand,
And we'll see our father's ships to land.'

She's ta'en her by the lily hand,
And led her down to the river-strand.

The youngest stood upon a stane,
The eldest cam and push'd her in.

'O sister, sister, reach your hand!
And ye sall be heir o' half my land:

'O sister, reach me but your glove!
And sweet William sall be your love.'—

'Foul fa' the hand that I should take;
It twin'd me o' my warldis make.

'Your cherry cheeks and your yellow hair
Gar'd me gang maiden evermair.'

Sometimes she sank, sometimes she swam,
Until she cam to the miller's dam.

twin'd, robbed.   *my warldis make*, my one mate in the world.

Out then cam the miller's son,
And saw the fair maid soummin' in.

'O father, father, draw your dam!
There's either a mermaid or a milk-white swan.'

The miller hasted and drew his dam,
And there he found a drown'd woman.

You couldna see her middle sma',
Her gowden girdle was sae braw.

You couldna see her lily feet,
Her gowden fringes were sae deep.

You couldna see her yellow hair
For the strings o' pearls was twisted there.

You couldna see her fingers sma',
Wi' diamond rings they were cover'd a'.

And by there cam a harper fine,
That harpit to the king at dine.

And when he look'd that lady on,
He sigh'd and made a heavy moan.

He's made a harp of her breast-bane,
Whose sound would melt a heart of stane.

He's ta'en three locks o' her yellow hair,
And wi' them strung his harp sae rare.

He went into her father's hall,
And there was the court assembled all.

He laid his harp upon a stane,
And straight it began to play by lane.

'O yonder sits my father, the King,
And yonder sits my mother, the Queen;

'And yonder stands my brother Hugh,
And by him my William, sweet and true.'

But the last tune that the harp play'd then—
    Binnorie, O Binnorie!
Was, 'Woe to my sister, false Helen!'
    By the bonnie milldams o' Binnorie.

BALLAD

90 *Heather Ale*

FROM the bonny bells of heather
    They brewed a drink long-syne,
Was sweeter far than honey,
    Was stronger far than wine.
They brewed it and they drank it,
    And lay in a blessed swound
For days and days together
    In their dwellings underground.

There rose a king in Scotland,
    A fell man to his foes,
He smote the Picts in battle,
    He hunted them like roes.
Over miles of the red mountain
    He hunted as they fled,
And strewed the dwarfish bodies
    Of the dying and the dead.

Summer came in the country,
    Red was the heather bell;
But the manner of the brewing
    Was none alive to tell.

In graves that were like children's
  On many a mountain head,
The Brewsters of the Heather
  Lay numbered with the dead.

The king in the red moorland
  Rode on a summer's day;
And the bees hummed, and the curlews
  Cried beside the way.
The king rode, and was angry,
  Black was his brow and pale,
To rule in a land of heather
  And lack the Heather Ale.

It fortuned that his vassals,
  Riding free on the heath,
Came on a stone that was fallen
  And vermin hid beneath.
Rudely plucked from their hiding,
  Never a word they spoke:
A son and his aged father—
  Last of the dwarfish folk.

The king sat high on his charger,
  He looked on the little men;
And the dwarfish and swarthy couple
  Looked at the king again.
Down by the shore he had them;
  And there on the giddy brink—
'I will give you life, ye vermin,
  For the secret of the drink.'

There stood the son and father
  And they looked high and low;
The heather was red around them,
  The sea rumbled below.

170

And up and spoke the father,
  Shrill was his voice to hear:
'I have a word in private,
  A word for the royal ear.

'Life is dear to the aged,
  And honour a little thing;
I would gladly sell the secret,'
  Quoth the Pict to the king.
His voice was small as a sparrow's,
  And shrill and wonderful clear;
'I would gladly sell my secret,
  Only my son I fear.

'For life is a little matter,
  And death is nought to the young
And I dare not sell my honour
  Under the eye of my son.
Take him, O king, and bind him,
  And cast him far in the deep;
And it's I will tell the secret
  That I have sworn to keep.'

They took the son and bound him,
  Neck and heels in a thong,
And a lad took him and swung him,
  And flung him far and strong,
And the sea swallowed his body.
  Like that of a child of ten;—
And there on the cliff stood the father,
  Last of the dwarfish men.

'True was the word I told you:
  Only my son I feared;
For I doubt the sapling courage
  That goes without the beard.

But now in vain is the torture,
   Fire shall never avail:
Here dies in my bosom
   The secret of Heather Ale.'

R. L. STEVENSON

91 *Proud Maisie*

PROUD Maisie is in the wood,
   Walking so early;
Sweet Robin sits on the bush,
   Singing so rarely.

'Tell me, thou bonny bird,
   When shall I marry me?'
—'When six braw gentlemen
   Kirkward shall carry ye.'

'Who makes the bridal bed,
   Birdie, say truly?'
—'The grey-headed sexton
   That delves the grave duly.

'The glow-worm o'er grave and stone
   Shall light thee steady;
The owl from the steeple sing
   Welcome, proud lady!'

SIR W. SCOTT

92 *Two Rivers*

SAYS Tweed to Till—
'What gars ye rin sae still?'
Says Till to Tweed—
'Though ye rin with speed
And I rin slaw,
For ae man that ye droon
I droon twa.'

BALLAD

93 *The Knight's Tomb*

WHERE is the grave of Sir Arthur O'Kellyn?
Where may the grave of that good man be?—
By the side of a spring, on the breast of Helvellyn,
Under the twigs of a young birch tree!
The oak that in summer was sweet to hear,
And rustled its leaves in the fall of the year,
And whistled and roared in the winter alone,
Is gone,—and the birch in its stead is grown.—
The Knight's bones are dust,
And his good sword rust;—
His soul is with the saints, I trust.

S. T. COLERIDGE

NOTES

The poems in this book have been arranged to form a continuous though varied pattern, and the reader will find links of various kinds. The notes that follow are concerned only with such facts and explanation as may help toward the understanding of the poems themselves. References are to the *numbers* of the poems.

1. GRAMARYE: enchantment.

2. LONG TRICK: turn of duty, life.

3. QUINQUIREME: ancient galley with five sets of rowers. 'Solomon . . . had a navy of Tarshish . . . bringing gold and silver, ivory and apes, and peacocks' (1 Kings xxii.) John Masefield (Poet Laureate 1930–) was once a sailor, and has written many poems about the sea, as well as stories such as *Jim Davis* and narrative poems such as *Reynard the Fox*.

5. One of Edward Lear's nonsense poems. Others are *The Jumblies* and *The Pobble Who Has No Toes*. RUNCIBLE: No known meaning, though a pickle fork has been named after it.

6. Longfellow made these verses to follow almost exactly an account by King Alfred the Great, in Anglo-Saxon, which tells how 'Othere told his lord, King Alfred, that he northmost of all the Northmen dwelt. . . .'

8. Without verbs or much grammar, this presents the description of the long wave and trough of mid-ocean, as you might see it from the port-hole of a liner, till it breaks into the over-running foam, 'hush-hushing, hush-hushing . . .'.

9. The accent here is on the *last* syllable of 'Trafalgar'. THE NOTHE: the headland sheltering Weymouth harbour.

10. A song from *The Tempest* (Act I, sc. ii), sung by Ariel to the bewildered young Prince Ferdinand:

> 'Weeping again the king my father's wreck,
> This music crept by me upon the waters.'

11. William Cowper, who wrote *John Gilpin* and many well-known hymns, lived in retirement after a mental breakdown. See also No. 84.

12. Ogden Nash is an American humorous poet.

14. This is, of course, an abstract cat, Care; and other abstract ideas are also personified. THE BLUE BIRD: happiness.

20. A clever example of the use of onomatopoeia.

24. THE LAVE: the remainder, all the rest.

25. Rum, Mull, and Eigg are islands off the west coast of Scotland.

29. Ecclesiastes xii. The images refer to growing old, e.g. 'those that look out of the windows' are the eyes; 'the almond tree' is white hair; and 'the grinders' are not only the corn-grinders, but the teeth. This is metaphor.

30. CHIMBORAZO, COTOPAXI: volcanoes in Ecuador. POPOCATAPETL: a volcano in Mexico. The poet was thinking of the Aztecs of Mexico, whom Cortes conquered, with their gold and strange temples, and perhaps of the Incas of Peru.

32. A fabulous journey, such as Ulysses and his men took, who came to the isle of Polyphemus the Cyclops; or Sir John Mandeville, whose *Voyages* owe more to legend than to reality. PRESTER JOHN: a legendary Christian king supposed to reign somewhere beyond Persia.

34. Edgar Allen Poe, American poet, and author of *Tales of Mystery and Imagination*. GHOULS: Eastern demons that prey upon the dead.

37. The last line recalls Christ's entry into Jerusalem 'mounted upon an ass's colt'.

38. From *The Second Jungle Book*. Mowgli was brought up by the wolf pack, and this is the Law taught him by Baloo the old brown bear. HATHI: elephant.

41. The title means 'The war-song (or pipe-music) of Donald the Black'.

42. CORONACH: dirge. CORREI: a mountain hollow or valley. CUMBER: hiding.

43. A Jacobite song, to Bonnie Prince Charlie.

44. In the first of these three rousing choruses we have the King's men marching to Nottingham to raise the Royal Standard in 1642 at the

beginning of the Civil War. PYM, HAMPDEN, &c.: leaders of the Parliamentary side. In the second, an old Cavalier remembers his son, whom the Roundheads killed. NOLL: Oliver Cromwell. GIVE A ROUSE: give a toast. For an expression of the opposite viewpoint, read Macaulay's *Battle of Naseby*.

45. This disastrous charge was at Balaclava, during the Crimean War, in 1854.

46. Agincourt was fought in 1415 and is celebrated also in Shakespeare's *Henry V*. The sixth verse refers to Poitiers (1356), and Cressy (or Crecy), ten years earlier than that, two victories of the Black Prince and his father Edward III.

47. King Tarquin, driven from Rome in 510 B.C., has called Lars Porsena, the Etruscan, to help him in reconquering the city.

48. From *Love's Labour's Lost*. SAW: wise saying, tag. KEEL: skim. CRABS: crab apples.

49. Robert Frost is an American poet, many of whose poems are set in the New England countryside.

50. A song from *As You Like It* (Act II, sc. vii).

51. A parody of *Sea Fever* (No. 2).

54. From *Pippa Passes*. As she goes by, her innocent songs have various effects upon those who hear them.

55. The oldest piece in this volume, an old song, the first in English to which musical notation is appended. It was probably written early in the thirteenth century.

58. PAWNEES, BLACKFEET: Indian tribes that once lived on the prairies, like the bison.

59. There are many stories of Hiawatha, the Red Indian hero, in Longfellow's poem, such as his search for his father, Mudjekeewis, the West Wind.

60. Another parody. Longfellow tells:

> He had mittens, Minjekahwun,
> Magic mittens made of deer-skin;
> When upon his hands he wore them,
> He could smite the rocks asunder.

61. From *The Second Jungle Book*.

63. THE GENTLEMEN: the smugglers. VALENCIENNES: lace, also dutiable. The little girl to whom the poem is addressed lived, perhaps, at some farm near the Sussex coast, or in a smugglers' haunt like 'Jamaica Inn' in the West Country. Clashes with the 'Preventives' were often bitter and bloody.

64. COLIBRIS: humming-birds. PIRAGUA: dug-out canoe, 'Buccaneers' were originally men who 'boucanned' or smoked beef on a gridiron, but soon became known as piratical adventurers, in the seventeenth century.

65. The *Revenge* fought her last fight in 1594. 'Fifteen Spanish ships were beaten off in turn; two were sunk, two disabled, and 2,000 men slain or drowned.'

66. W. S. Gilbert wrote the words of the 'Gilbert and Sullivan' operas. This poem was refused publication by *Punch* as being 'too canni-balistic' for the taste of its readers.

67. An old ballad, like *Lord Randall* (No. 87), *Chevy Chase*, or *Binnorie*. These are ancient poems, of unknown authorship, many of them dealing with wild or strange happenings near the Scottish Border; and many are in dialect. Some have refrains, or little repetitive tags, like nursery rhymes. This verse-form, *abcb*, with lines of four beats and three beats alternately, is called 'ballad metre'.

70. CAMELOT: where King Arthur held his court, perhaps in Somerset, though Malory states that it was Winchester. WILLOWS WHITEN: as the wind turns the light underside of the leaves.

71. GALLIARD: a dance.

72. This poem, in ballad style, is set in the time of the Indian Mutiny.

74. Sir Jonathan Trelawny, of a famous Cornish family, was one of the seven bishops tried by James II, and acquitted after much public fervour.

75. See Isaiah xxxvii.

76. Vachel Lindsay, the American poet, who also wrote No. 58, used to provide his audiences with glass lamp-chimneys when they read the

Daniel Jazz in chorus so that they could roar like the lions at the appropriate time. See also *The Congo* in Book III.

77. Psalm xix.

78. The author was once a hobo, and wrote *The Autobiography of a Super-Tramp*.

79. The names are those of streets in the City of London.

81. A lullaby sung over the sleeping Titania, Queen of the Fairies, in *A Midsummer Night's Dream* (Act II, sc. ii). PHILOMEL: the nightingale.

85. JENNET: a small Spanish horse.

86. From *Alice Through the Looking-Glass*.

87. Old ballad. Direct speech, almost dramatic dialogue, is a characteristic of these poems.

88. This is, of course, metaphor, or allegory. John Barleycorn is the barley; and his blood is whisky, or perhaps beer.

ANALYTICAL LIST OF POEMS

(The numbers are those of the poems)

BALLADS (a) Old Ballads, 67, 87, 89, 92.
      (b) Ballad Poems, 71, 72, 88.
      (c) Old Songs, 4, 23, 43, 55, 83.

BATTLE AND WAR, 9, 41–47, 65, 72.

CHORAL AND MIME, 20, 33, 34, 44, 55, 57, 76, 87, 89.

COUNTRYSIDE, OPEN AIR, 1, 16, 19–21, 23–25, 52–57, 70, 78–81, 84.

CREATURES, 11–13, 15, 20–22, 35–39, 58.

DIALECT, 4, 26, 27, 43, 55, 76, 89, 92.

HISTORICAL, 6, 9, 43–47, 62–65, 72–74.

HUMOUR, PARODY, NONSENSE, 5, 11–14, 22, 27, 32, 39, 40, 48, 51, 60, 66, 86.

LAMENTS, 7, 11, 25, 35, 36, 42, 43, 50, 58, 68, 69, 84, 91, 93.

NARRATIVE, 4–6, 12, 22, 27, 32, 40, 45–47, 59, 64–68, 70–73, 75, 76, 86–90.

PEOPLE, 6, 7, 24, 26, 70, 79, 87.

SEA, 1–10, 18, 25, 32, 64–68, 82.

SEASONS (a) Spring, 19, 20, 51, 53–55, 57, 80.
      (b) Autumn, 17, 52, 56, 70.
      (c) Winter, 48–50, 69.

YOUTH AND AGE, 1, 13, 25–31, 63, 82, 85.

CHRONOLOGICAL LIST OF AUTHORS

The period to which each author is assigned is that during which he wrote the majority of his poems included in this volume.

EARLY POEMS: Ballads (67, 87, 89, 92); Old Songs (4, 23, 55).

SIXTEENTH AND EARLY SEVENTEENTH CENTURIES. The Bible (29, 77); T. Dekker (33); M. Drayton (46); R. Herrick (83); T. Heywood (19); W. Shakespeare (10, 48, 50, 57, 81).

EIGHTEENTH CENTURY. R. Burns (26, 88); W. Cowper (11, 84).

EARLY NINETEENTH CENTURY. R. Barham (22); Lord Byron (75); S. T. Coleridge (93); T. Hood (28); Lady Nairne (43); E. A. Poe (34); Sir W. Scott (41, 42, 71, 91); P. B. Shelley (69); W. Wordsworth (53, 79, 80).

LATER NINETEENTH CENTURY. M. Arnold (68); R. Browning (40, 44, 54, 73); L. Carroll (86); W. S. Gilbert (66); R. S. Hawker (74); C. Kingsley (7, 64); E. Lear (5); H. W. Longfellow (6, 59); Lord Macaulay (47); R. L. Stevenson (17, 24, 25, 90); Lord Tennyson (20, 21, 45, 65, 70, 82).

TWENTIETH CENTURY. G. F. Bradby (51); R. Brooke (39); G. K. Chesterton (37); W. H. Davies (78); W. de la Mare (16, 31, 52); R. Frost (49); T. Hardy (9, 56); R. Hodgson (35, 85); R. Hughes (14); R. Kipling (38, 61, 63); V. Lindsay (58, 76); J. Masefield (2, 3); H. Monro (13); C. Morley (1); C. Murray (27); O. Nash (12); Sir H. Newbolt (72); A. Noyes (18, 32, 62); J. Stephens (8, 36); W. J. Turner (30); W. B. Yeats (15); Anon. (60).

INDEX OF AUTHORS AND TITLES

184

185

INDEX OF FIRST LINES